£4.99

THE TROPICAL AGRICULTURALIST

Series Editor
René Coste
Formerly President of the IRCC

D0529820

Coffee Growing

H. R. Cambrony
Tropical Agronomist

Translated by Shirley Barrett
With advice from John Mburu Njoroge,
Coffee Research Foundation, Kenya
Translation edited by Professor H. D. Tindall
Illustrations by Michel Cambrony

CTA MACMILLAN

Original French edition published in 1989 under the
title *Le Cafeier*
in the series *Le Technicien d'Agriculture Tropicale,*
by the ACCT and Maisonneuve et Larose,
15 rue Victor-Cousin, 75005 Paris, France.
No responsibility is taken by the holders of the copyright
for any changes to the original French text.

This edition published by THE MACMILLAN PRESS LTD
London and Basingstoke
Associated companies and representatives in Accra,
Auckland, Delhi, Dublin, Gaborone, Hamburg, Harare,
Hong Kong, Kuala Lumpur, Lagos, Manzini, Melbourne,
Mexico City, Nairobi, New York, Singapore, Tokyo

Published in co-operation with the Technical Centre for
Agricultural and Rural Co-operation, PO Box 380,
700 AJ Wageningen, The Netherlands.

ISBN 0–333–54451–X

Phototypeset by Intype, London

Printed in Hong Kong

A CIP catalogue record for this book is available from
the British Library

The opinions expressed in this document and the spellings of
proper names and territorial boundaries are solely the
responsibility of the authors and in no way involve the
official position or the liability of the Agency for Cultural
and Technical Co-operation or the Technical Centre for
Agricultural and Rural Co-operation.

Cover illustration Courtesy of Frank Lane Photograph Agency

About this book

This volume covers the botany of the coffee plant, and how to grow and harvest coffee. A further volume in the series will cover the processing of coffee beans and the manufacture and marketing of finished coffee.

The Technical Centre for Agricultural and Rural Co-operation (CTA) operates under the Lomé Convention between member States of the European Community and the African, Caribbean and Pacific (ACP) States.

The aim of CTA is to collect, disseminate and facilitate the exchange of information on research, training and innovations in the spheres of agricultural and rural development and extension, for the benefit of the ACP states.

To achieve this aim, CTA:
- commissions and publishes studies;
- organises and supports conferences, workshops and courses;
- supports publications and translations;
- offers an extensive information service.

Postal address: Postbus 380, 6700 AJ Wageningen, Netherlands
Telephone: 31–0–8380–20484
Telex: 44–30169 CTA NL
Fax: 31–0–8380–31052

Agency for Cultural and Technical Co-operation (ACCT)

The Agency for Cultural and Technical Co-operation, an intergovernmental organisation set up by the Treaty of Niamey in March 1970, is an association of countries linked by their common usage of the French language, for the purposes of co-operation in the fields of education, culture, science and technology and, more generally, in all matters which contribute to the development of its Member States and to bringing peoples closer together.

The Agency's activities in the fields of scientific and technical co-operation for development are directed primarily towards the preparation, dissemination and exchange of scientific and technical information, drawing up an inventory of and exploiting natural resources, and the socioeconomic advancement of young people and rural communities.

Member countries: Belgium, Benin, Burundi, Canada, Central African Republic, Chad, Comoros, Congo, Djibouti, Dominica, France, Gabon, Guinea, Haiti, Ivory Coast, Lebanon, Luxembourg, Mali, Mauritius, Monaco, Niger, Rwanda, Senegal, Seychelles, Togo, Tunisia, Burkina Faso, Vanuatu, Viet Nam, Zaire.

Associated States: Cameroon, Egypt, Guinea-Bissau, Laos, Mauritania, Morocco, St Lucia.

Participating governments: New Brunswick, Quebec.

Contents

Preface

This handbook has been written for agricultural extension workers and coffee growers who wish to improve their traditional working practices. Written originally in French, it has been translated, and edited in English by Professor H. D. Tindall, formerly of Silsoe College, now a tropical agronomy consultant. We are very grateful for his input.

The aim of this book is to supply the reader with full information collected from the most reliable scientific sources and presented in a simple and amply illustrated form so as to improve his/her knowledge of the coffee plant and its growing methods. Proper use of this information under appropriate environmental conditions is, in fact, likely to increase yield and improve the quality of the product.

It is hoped that this information will pave the way to more intensive agriculture, resulting in better profit per unit area, while releasing arable land on farms which would then be available for other crops (various food or industrial crops). It also aims to enable the adoption, on farms in tropical countries, of the developments in rural progress already made on farms in temperate regions, owing to the planting of selected seed and to the use of more effective production methods, materials and post-harvest treatments, as resulting from agricultural research findings.

However, this guide, which is essentially a practical one, reflects the selections made by the author from the huge body of information on a subject made complex by its variety and already dealt with in detail in encyclopaedic volumes. Consequently, the scientific, economic and statistical considerations will be limited to information essential to an understanding of the recommended methods; the botanical and biological sections in particular refer only to the two main species grown, arabica and canephora, although certain digressions will be made to discuss their hybrids, the arabustas.

Elsewhere, from the technical point of view, repetitive details concerning non-specific horticultural operations, such as land clearance, creation of service paths, pegging and nursery layout, etc., already described in the volumes in the series or widely covered in traditional agricultural teaching, have only been referred to briefly.

An attempt has been made to demonstrate the advantages and disadvantages of each of the techniques mentioned, when there is an alternative, as regards their degree of suitability for any particular species or variety, a given ecological environment or a given production system.

Much has therefore been left for the reader's judgement so as to enable him/her to assess the possibilities of transposing the recommended cultural techniques, in order to bring them more into conformity with the particular features of the land and the economic and social circumstances of the farms involved. It concerns the skill of the well-informed farmer and is one of the fundamental bases of successful production.

We hope that the various aspects selected by the author, presented in this way, will meet the needs of the reader.

1 Introduction

1.1 A brief history and economics of coffee

There is now no longer any doubt that the coffee plant originated in Africa. Arabica coffee, despite its name, comes from Ethiopia and is still found in wild populations in the undergrowth of the high Abyssinian plateaux. The canephora species also grow wild in the evergreen forests which stretch from Central Africa to West Africa; the liberica and similar species occupy the margins of the same areas.

Originally used in a biscuit containing dried fruit mixed with butter called the Abyssinian 'bun', it was only a little later that users had the idea of enjoying its stimulant properties in an infusion of the roasted and ground beans in boiling water.

We owe this preparation (Kavah – then Kaveh in Turkish) to the Arabs, as we do the history of its cultivation.

With the exception of Ethiopia and Uganda, where the coffee plant grew in woodland or in small gardens, it was not until the nineteenth century that the Europeans extended its cultivation and commercialisation into Africa. This was achieved by using the arabica species in the favourable mountainous regions, and naturalised and indigenous West African species such as liberica and canephora in their wild form found in the Congo. These were sold under the well-justified name of robusta.

Since then, despite some fluctuation, the development of coffee cultivation has been unstoppable in all areas where it is ecologically possible and economically advantageous to grow it.

Coffee research has enabled selected varieties or **cultivars** to be added to the indigenous species, and, very recently, new interspecific genetic combinations have been created.

Why has coffee been so successful? There is no doubt that, for the consumer, it produces a beverage with stimulating and mood-elevating properties which are so well known that new countries, sometimes traditionally dedicated to tea (Japan and Eastern countries), are now becoming converted to the highly-valued bean. However, for the producers of

1

the tropical Third World, it is also a raw material of great economic and social importance.

In world trade terms, although it is overtaken by cereals in tonnage, in value terms, in commercial dealings, it follows closely after oil.

It is an important earner of strong currencies, contributing in varying degrees to the national income of the producing countries for which, unlike the food crops of self-sufficiency, it guarantees a solid basis for the promotion of economic development. It is this role which, historically, it has played in Brazil and which it is still playing in some of the relatively unindustrialised countries of Central America or Africa, for example Colombia, Costa Rica, Rwanda, Ivory Coast, Kenya, Cameroon.

Production lies mainly in the hands of a large number of small planters, there being few large private or state industrial plantations hence its great social importance. Brazil and Kenya do, however, have large private operations, while Indonesia has some nationalised plantations. Coffee production has undergone rapid expansion, four or five years being sufficient for production to get underway, but it is subject to sharp decreases. This may be attributable to climatic conditions, e.g. the severe frosts of 1975 in Brazil in particular, or those resulting from political troubles, a case in question being Angola: 30 000 tonnes per year after the war of independence compared with 200 000 tonnes per year previously. This was also true for production in Uganda when it was suddenly affected by political instability.

The arabica species predominates, representing 66 per cent or 75 per cent of the total, both in terms of production and export, but the robusta species is playing an increasingly important role in trade, from 25 per cent to 30 per cent of the total production, encouraged by the popularity of instant coffee where its greater yield per unit area is in its favour.

On the face of it, there has been a slow but regular increase in **world consumption** of just less than 3 per cent per annum since the end of the second world war. This is in line with demographic expansion in the large, traditional, coffee consuming countries (USA, EEC and Scandinavia), as well as with the general rise in the standard of living. From 1973, this was offset by the economic crisis affecting first of all the large oil-consuming countries and then the oil-producing countries themselves. These local recessions are manifested in the form of stagnation, or even a decline in national consumption of coffee. Another negative factor which should be pointed out is the growth in competition from other drinks, especially among young consumers.

Domestic consumption in the producing countries varies enormously. It is very high in Brazil, accounting for approximately 20 per cent of the coffee produced, and in the Latin American countries, but remains very low in Africa and Asia.

Periodical surges in overproduction result in sudden drops in price.

This leads governments to try to stabilise prices for the producer so as to avoid socio-economic problems. These price stabilisation efforts were finally ratified by the U.N. by the drawing up of a general agreement by the International Coffee Organization (ICO), with its headquarters in London, of which almost all the producing and consuming countries were members. This agreement was based on the allocation of annual export quotas to each producing country; these were flexible according to their effect on world prices. Regrettably, the ICO was disbanded in 1990 and it is not yet clear what results this action will have on world prices and the previously regulated quotas.

1.2 Classification and external structure

The botanists Linnaeus and De Jussieu described *Coffea arabica* and placed it in the Rubiaceae family. The genus *Coffea* contains approximately 70 species, of which the most widely grown are the *Arabica* and *Canephora* species.

Shoot system

The shape of coffee bushes vary enormously depending on the species or variety (Fig 1). The aerial organs given them their characteristic shape.

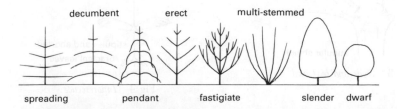

decumbent   erect   multi-stemmed

spreading   pendant   fastigiate   slender   dwarf

Fig 1   *Different growth habits of coffee plants*

The stem is erect, **orthotropic** (vertical), and sometimes multiple, caused by the development of suckers arising from buds at the base of the trunk.

Opposite branches, more or less **plagiotropic** (horizontal), are inserted **helically** on the stem. These subdivide into more or less **flexuose** (slender) secondary and sometimes tertiary branches (arabica), composed of internodes of varying length, depending on the species. Stem length is limited by the number of nodes from which arise the **petioles** (stalks) of two opposite leaves. The triangular **stipular sheath** which protects the axillary buds, is situated between the trunk and the base of the petiole.

3

Opposite pairs of **lanceolate** leaves with an **acuminate** (gradually diminishing) apex, are supported by a short petiole with nine to eleven veins on the lamina. The leaves vary in shape, texture and colour depending on the species and variety.

Axillary buds on the stem comprise a **primary bud** from which only the plagiotropic branches arise (Fig 2), together with fixed numbers of buds which provide suckers, orthotropic suckers and inflorescences (Fig 3). Axillary buds on the branches normally give rise to inflorescences or vegetative growth. Additional buds may be formed.

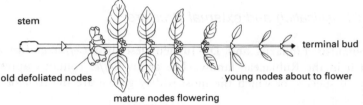

Fig 2   *Branch of coffee plant showing centrifugal development (fruiting on one year old wood)*

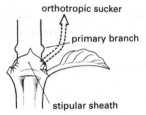

Fig 3   *Node and leaf axil*

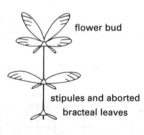

Fig 4   *Inflorescence*

There are three to five or more inflorescences per leaf axil. The twigs terminate in a flower bud (Fig 4).

The Flowers are generally **pentamerous** (parts in fives) and are borne on a short pedicel. Thus, they are referred to as sessile or subsessile flowers. Two or three pairs of foliaceous bracteoles may be attached. Each flower consists of:

- a small calyx, the lobes of which are notched;
- a **fugacious** (short-lived) white corolla, arranged in a tube opening out into five lobes;
- an inferior, globular ovary, with a fleshy disc at the apex (scar), consisting of two loculi, each containing an ovule. The ovary is surmounted by a style, inserted into the centre of the disc. This is divided into two **stigmata** (linear branches);

- linear anthers, attached to the base of the petaloid lobes by a short filament; the anthers and filaments together comprise the stamen.

Figures 5 and 6 illustrate the components of a flower. The fertilised flower a produces a drupe, commonly called a 'cherry' because of its shape and colour.

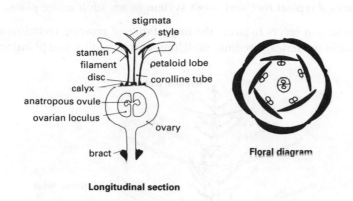

Fig 5   *Single flower*

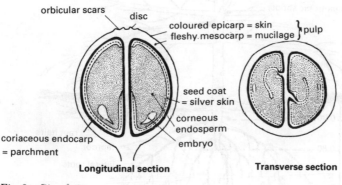

Fig 6   *Ripe fruit*

Root system

The role of the root system is to ensure that the plant is firmly anchored in the ground and receives a supply of water and minerals. It consists of:

5

- a short **taproot** (0.4 to 0.6 cm), several taproots are sometimes formed in rocky soils;
- vertical, **coaxial roots**, four to eight in number, which are often very long, particularly in a light soil with a deep water table, e.g. Brazilian 'terra rosa' soils;
- downward growing **lateral roots**, with innumerable absorbing **root hairs**, particularly in the upper, humus-bearing layer (0–30 cm). Fig 7 illustrates a typical root and shoot system in an adult coffee plant.

This information serves to stress the importance of growing techniques (pricking out in nurseries, weeding, mulching and irrigation and planting

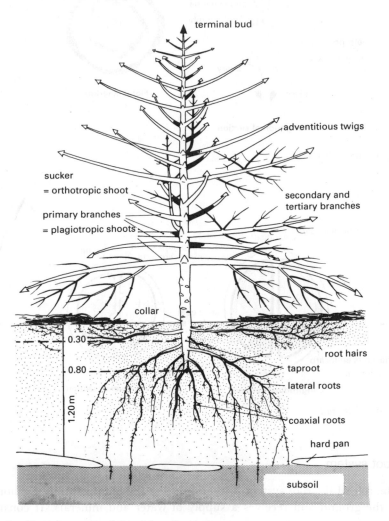

Fig 7 *Typical structure of the adult coffee plant*

layouts) on the distribution and function of the roots. This is also related to the nature of the soil (the presence of a hard pan or lateritic gravel, texture of the soil, depth of the subsoil layer, etc.) and sometimes to the climate, e.g. development of deep roots in arid areas.

1.3 Growth and development

This section describes the developmental phases of the coffee plant. These are dependent on internal, eco-physiological factors and also on its environment. They include the growth, flowering, fruiting and, subsequently, the death of the coffee plant.

Growth phase of the young plant

The **seed** of the coffee plant is the coffee bean, whether covered with its parchment or not. It is characterised by its ability to germinate, the success rate may be 90 per cent when it is fresh, decreasing rapidly, particularly from four months onwards in its natural environment. However, seeds may still be viable after four years when stored at + 10°C, in an atmosphere of 50 per cent relative humidity. A water content of over 10 per cent is necessary to retain viability; this is achieved by moderate drying under shade.

Germination requires a humid environment, which facilitates the imbibition of water by the seed. Enzymes within the seed are then activated and trigger the development of the embryo. Appearance at the soil surface takes place owing to the growth of the radicle which, over a period of 25 – 30 days, pushes the seed above the ground. The cotyledonary leaves develop while the growing point remains relatively dormant. This is called **epigeal germination** (Fig 8).

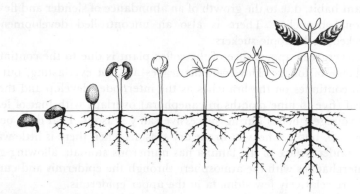

Fig 8   *Stages in development of the seedling*

7

Growth of the young plant is initially at the expense of the cotyledonary reserves. It continues to grow in height until the first branches are formed. This occurs from the fifth to the eleventh pair of leaves in robusta. The cotyledonary leaves wither and fall approximately four to six weeks after appearing above the ground.

At the age of approximately one year, the young plant has four to eight pairs of branches. The shoot system now has all its vegetative structures, i.e. terminal bud, axillary buds and foliage on the branches. The annual growth rhythm is, from this stage, closely linked to the climatic conditions; the alternation of the wet and dry seasons regulates this growth; vegetative dormancy during the dry season prepares for and induces flowering.

Productivity phase

The young plant continues to grow for up to two or three years, by which time a specific balance between the shoot and the root system has been achieved which is appropriate for maturity and flowering. This reproductive phase enables the first crop to be picked in the third year. Thereafter, the annual flowering – fruiting rhythm superimposes itself on the rate of vegetative growth. The plant is then complete, both physiologically and economically. It is considered to be fully mature when it is five to six years old. It is then close to 3 m in height, although it is often pruned down to 2 m for convenience in harvesting.

The main assimilatory function (photosynthesis) takes place in the leaves as do also respiration and evapotranspiration.

The major plant functions are mainly based on the framework of the tree, consisting of either a single or multiple stem and its primary, secondary and tertiary branches. The importance of the secondary branches for training and fruiting in the arabica varieties should be noted.

As time passes, there is generally a progressive change in the regular structure of the young plant, which would normally have a drooping or **pendant** habit, due to the growth of an abundance of slender and flexible additional branches. There is also an uncontrolled development of unchecked, orthotropic suckers.

The evergreen appearance of the coffee plant is due to the continuous abundance of foliage. However, the leaves are not everlasting, but leaf growth continues on the branches as the internodes develop and the life of a leaf (five to nine months in canephora) overlaps with that of leaves of the youngest nodes during successive rainy seasons. Leaf drop occurs all the time, but it is heavier in the dry seasons when there is little water.

The undersurface of the lamina has numerous stomata allowing gaseous interchanges with the atmosphere through the epidermis and cuticle. There are relatively few stomata in the upper epidermis.

The efficiency of the leaves in photosynthesis and in transpiration depends on the density of the stomata and their closure mechanism, as well as the permeability of the cuticles and the pigmentation of the lamina. These characteristics, which vary greatly between arabica and canephora, largely explain why the two species adapt very differently to ecological conditions.

The regulation of the water content within the plant involves a balance being achieved between the rates of root absorption and transpiration from the leaves. An excess of the latter leads to the wilting of the leaves on the branch and subsequently the entire plant.

Flowering

Flowering enables the species to reproduce itself as well as leading to the production of edible berries. The structural information has described the location and form of the flowering organs. The details of the wood bearing the inflorescences should be remembered, i.e. one-year-old wood, situated in particular on the primary branches in canephora, and on both the primary and secondary branches in arabica.

Full development, from the appearance of the floral node to the opening of the clustered flower-heads, takes at least two and a half months. In fact, only the final phase (transition from the green bud stage to the open, white bud stage) is of fixed duration. For example, in the sub-equatorial conditions of the Ivory Coast, the final phase takes six to seven days in canephora and arabusta.

There may be one or two flowering periods, triggered by sudden rains, which may occur during the dry season (*C. canephora*) or at the beginning of the rainy season (*C. arabica*), but minor additional flowering may occur, particularly in climates with four seasons.

One anomaly in flower development, called star flowering, consists of the premature opening of the flower buds during their final stage of pre-flowering. If opening is very early, it generally leads to the flower becoming sterile. This anomaly reveals an instance of poor ecological adaptation by the species, as is the case with arabicas in low-lying, hot and humid equatorial areas.

Pollination

This is brought about by insects such as bees and ants, the wind and gravity, particularly in the case of the arabicas when the pollen from the flowers on the upper branches falls onto the stigmata of the flowers on the lower branches.

Pollen has a relatively short life (three to four days under normal conditions). This life can be extended by keeping the pollen in a cool, dry place, in a glass or plastic container.

9

> *Clonal plantations of robusta (cuttings or grafts) require the interplanting of pollinating coffee plants or the use of clonal mixtures, without which they are not productive.*

Fruiting

The development of the fruiting ovary begins with the development of the **perisperm**, the cellular tissue enveloping the ovule. It is characterised by an enlargement of the ovary, corresponding to the apparent first stage in the formation of the fruit. The development of the endosperm then takes place, creating the albumen and compressing the cells of the perisperm, which will only continue to exist at the periphery of the loculus in the form of a skin of dead cells filled with air, known as the silver skin.

Approximately six weeks after flowering, the embryo starts to develop. This is the phase which actually initiates the formation of the fruit.

Up to the final ripening of the berries, by which time they will have developed a reddened epidermis, a period of six to eight months will have elapsed for *C. arabica* and nine to eleven months for *C. canephora*. High altitudes extend these average periods because of the lower temperatures found there. In the case of *C. arabica*, a delay of ten days has been recorded in Guinea for every 100 m increase in elevation above 900 m.

The growth rate of the fruit can be plotted as an S-shaped curve on a graph, showing three distinct periods:

I – from 0 to 8 weeks: slow growth.

II – from 8 to 24 weeks: rapid growth.

III – beyond 24 weeks: slow development, change in colour due to ripening.

A relatively small proportion (16 – 20 per cent) of all fertilised flowers reach the ripe fruit stage. Furthermore, when harvested, there remain on the tree a certain number of poorly developed fruits, these being wrinkled, pest-infested or deformed (the norm being two convex beans per fruit, i.e. one per loculus).

The following phenomena may occur:

- **Multiple embryos**: presence of beans with several embryos;
- **Multiple ovules**: two, or rarely more, fertilised ovules may develop in one loculus. This is termed 'elephants ears';
- **'Pea berry'**: rounded fruits with a single bean, following the fertilisation of the ovule of only one loculus.
- **Empty loculi**: fruit without seeds due to late abortion, with degeneration of the two seeds.
- **Scaling**: early abortion of a seed in a loculus.

It should be noted that alternating production or biennial bearing is a fairly common phenomenon for the mature coffee plant of five to six years. It is particularly pronounced if the growing conditions are not very satisfactory.

Senility – vegetative decline phase

This final stage in the life of the coffee plant can be identified by a gradual degeneration of the shoot system, and a serious fall in production, accompanied by the death of the root system. This usually takes place at a fairly advanced stage in the life of the plantation, depending on the way in which it is run and the care taken in its maintenance.

In commercial production, it is estimated that a coffee plant is no longer viable after 25 to 30 years of intensive cultivation, when the production costs will no longer be sufficiently offset by the reduced size of the crop. However, with good tree management, coffee can still be economically viable at over 100 years of age.

On a family plantation, under shade, with lower production levels this poor production phase may be prolonged, especially in a fertile soil and in the absence of serious damage to plant health.

It is therefore necessary to make sure that, in coffee-growing, biological longevity is not confused with economic longevity. Favourable environmental conditions and proper maintenance are likely, to some extent, to narrow the gap between them.

1.4 The ecology of coffee

This section studies the influence of the environment on the coffee plant, in particular the characteristics of natural factors such as climate and soil and their influence on development. Their effects determine the siting of indigenous species and the economic life of the plants, in other words their potential for profitable production and, by the same token, the distribution of the crops throughout the world.

Limiting ecological factors

The suitability of a given site for good coffee production is determined by four basic environmental variables: temperature, availability of water, light intensity and soil conditions. All other geographical conditions, such as latitude, altitude or topographical factors such as exposure or aspect, only affect the coffee plants insofar as they interact with the four basic variables. Another climatic element: air movement, does, however, play an important role in the way it affects the crops.

Temperature

No species can survive for long at a temperature of less than 0°C. Sensitivity to the cold does, however, vary according to the species. *C. arabica* is the most tolerant, being able to withstand a temperature of 2°C for up to six hours without damage. *C. canephora* varieties are more sensitive, with temperatures lower than + 5°C leading to dwarfing and leaf discoloration. At the other extreme, temperatures exceeding 30°C, are disastrous for all varieties of coffee plant.

The various species of coffee are normally to be found growing in temperatures between 18°C and 25°C, with fixed lower and upper limits of 15°C and 30°C respectively, which corresponds to most locations between the tropics of Capricorn and Cancer.

Altitude affects these average temperatures by a drop of 1°C for every 180 m of elevation.

Damage to vegetative growth due to excesses of temperature include:

- Death of branches, and sometimes the trunk, due to hard frosts in plants grown in Brazil, African Highlands and Madagascan or Vietnamese plateaux;
- 'Hot and cold disorder' of arabica coffee plants grown in Kenya, caused by the sharp variation in day and night-time temperatures.

Availability of water

This phenomena includes two factors: precipitation (rainfall) and humidity.

Rainfall and temperature together, are the two most important limiting factors in the life of the coffee plant.

Two aspects to consider are total monthly and annual rainfall levels and the way in which the precipitation is distributed. This emphasises the importance of the length of the dry season, which is the period of vegetative rest and flower induction. Limited to between three and four months for the canephora varieties, it can be up to six months for arabicas.

In the case of annual rainfall, 1200 to 2000 mm is a desirable range. Below 800 mm for arabicas and 1000 mm for canephoras can cause uncertainties in the economic life of the coffee plantations without additional irrigation.

Coffee plants adapt more successfully to excessive rainfall if the topography (slope) and physical characteristics of the ground allow for adequate drainage.

Humidity is measured in terms of relative humidity, vapour pressure or saturation deficit. A permanently high level of humidity is generally desirable. In the dry season, high atmospheric humidity at night (relative humidity of 80 – 100 per cent), often condensing into dew in the morning, possibly compensates for daytime dryness, when the relative humidity may fall to less than 30 – 50 per cent around midday.

Light

Wild coffee plants are naturally woodland plants found in high forests and are adapted to conditions of low light intensity.

In cultivation, shading was traditionally the norm, being a justified practice because, experimentally, it had been found that in the leaf, the yield from photosynthesis was at its maximum in reduced lighting conditions (between 10 per cent and 60 per cent of full sunlight), and that the stomata closed in bright sunlight. But, in fact, self-shading, provided by the over-lapping foliage, makes it unnecessary and even damaging to have artificial shading, particularly in the equatorial or subequatorial regions where there is a great deal of cloud cover.

Nowadays, coffee growers do not generally use shading, particularly in intensive, commercial cultivation.

Shade trees are still used, however, on a family plantation, either because of tradition, or because of necessity on account of the attendant advantages they bring, such as moderation of excesses of temperature, a reduction in erosion caused by rain, and as suppliers of mulch (after pruning in the dry season).

Air movement

Although, in general, a very light movement of air promotes gaseous exchange in the leaves, strong winds are harmful to the coffee plant.

Strong winds, tornadoes or cyclones, may cause structural damage, for instance defoliation, branches breaking, exposure of roots in light soils and even uprooting.

Less strong but permanent winds, e.g. trade winds, off-shore or on-shore breezes, mountain winds, accentuate the physiological drawbacks such as excessive evapotranspiration, die-back of the branches and early withering of the flowering parts or of the fruits close to ripening. The use of hedges forming a windbreak often proves to be essential.

Soil conditions

As far as soil conditions are concerned, coffee plants show great flexibility in their adaptation to soil types, and coffee plantations can be found on a large variety of soils, the fertility levels of which may, moreover, be modified by appropriate growing techniques such as fertilisers and irrigation.

> *The structure of the soil, its depth (ideally greater than 1.2 m above any obstacle: hard pan, sub-soil layer, bedrock) and its water-holding capacity are more important than its chemical fertility.*

It is important to note that acid soils (pH between 4.5 and 6.5) are considered to be favourable to growth. Below pH 4, liming and/or the application of magnesium limestone should be considered. Above pH 7 and up to pH 8, the humus will have to be renewed frequently by mulching, burying cover crops or manuring. Acidifying fertilisers (ammonium sulphate) will also have to be used.

Ecology of the cultivated species

C. arabica
The most suitable climate is the original (Ethiopian) climate, that is a tropical climate tempered by altitude, with two contrasting seasons; an average rainfall of 1500 mm to 1800 mm; a dry season lasting a maximum of six months and an average annual temperature of between 18°C and 22°C. In low-lying, hot and humid equatorial areas, star-flowering may occur. In these regions the altitude must be greater than 800 m for normal flower production to occur. Damage from hard frosts is possible in borderline areas, for example the State of Parana in Brazil, and there is a risk of hot and cold disorder at very high altitudes below the Equator, for instance in parts of Kenya.

C. canephora
This species requires a hot and humid equatorial to sub-equatorial climate with an average annual temperature of between 20°C and 25°C, and no large monthly or day/night swings. Heavy annual rainfall of between 1500 and 2500 mm, spread over nine to ten months, ensures excellent vegetative growth and fruiting. A fairly short dry season, however, is necessary for good flower development and fertilisation and high relative humidity is essential in all seasons.

Borderline growing areas, however, are to be found at latitudes relatively close to the tropics (the east coast of Madagascar or New Caledonia) on fertile alluvial soil at sea level. These have adequate rainfall but also have temperatures ranging from 8°C to 30°C.

A species related to C. canephora is Coffea congensis, which is peculiar in that it tolerates temporary waterlogging, a characteristic which is exploited in the hybrids with C. canephora, namely Congusta and Conuga.

The hybrids of the Arabusta type (C. arabica × C. canephora) also grow under the same ecological conditions as C. canephora, but are able to retain good leaf turgidity in drier climates. Their characteristics, on the other hand, resemble those of C. arabica in the Brazilian interspecific hybrids Icatu and Catimor.

Modifications made by agriculture

Horticultural modifications to marginal ecological conditions are always possible in the production of coffee, but they are limited and rather expensive. Agricultural science and plant breeding in particular, have overcome environmental problems in the following ways:

- By the selection of varieties resistant to dry conditions, to extremes of temperature, to excess water in the ground (hybrids of *C. congensis*, grafts/cuttings) and to diseases and predators;
- The selection of highly productive plants, suited to variable environments, resistant to different diseases and giving a product with good organoleptic properties has been the prime aim of researchers. Today we are able to appreciate the success of various selections obtained from the main species grown or their hybrids, which is the result of the research work carried out by agricultural experts.

Current distribution of the species

C. arabica: South and Central America, Caribbean, Islands in the Pacific, India, Indonesia, Viet Nam, New Guinea, the Philippines, highland areas of Africa; Ethiopia, Kenya, Tanzania, Zimbabwe, Rwanda, Burundi, Kivu (Zaire), Angola, Cameroon and Guinea.

C. Canephora (**Robusta**): Africa (relatively low, hot and humid areas), Uganda, Tanzania, Angola, Sudan, Zaire, Central African Republic, Cameroon, Congo, Gabon, Benin, Togo, Ghana, Ivory Coast, Guinea, Sierra Leone, India, Indonesia, New Caledonia, the Philippines, Vietnam, Cambodia, Brazil (Conilon), Bolivia and Trinidad.

2 Propagation and planting out

2.1 *Propagation*

In the high Ethiopian forests for *C. arabica* and in the west or central African forests for *C. canephora*, the natural propagation of coffee plants takes place by seeds falling to the ground below the mother plants, or by dispersal of the seeds by animals such as rats, squirrels and birds. Young plants propagated by the former method grow under dense shade beneath the parent plant. This environment usually results in etiolated seedlings, with long internodes and thin stems. It is strongly recommended that they are not used in plantations.

Propagation by selected seeds is more promising. Using appropriate nursery techniques, it is possible to produce vigorous, carefully selected plants, which guarantees that the plant will 'take' well and that the coffee plantation will be profitable.

Other methods can also be used, such as cuttings or grafts; their use is necessary if clonal plantations of high quality plants are to be created, or for the establishment of seed-bearing plots.

Propagation by seed

This system uses seedlings from selected parent trees which should be of clonal origin. A high proportion of these seedlings will be very similar to the clonal parents.

Selection and preparation of the seed

Seeds should be obtained from healthy, ripe fruit, selected from adult trees which are vigorous and have desirable characteristics.

The fruits should be carefully depulped, either manually or mechanically. They are then subjected to a short period of fermentation of less than 24 hours, after which they are rubbed under water to remove the remainder of the pulp still adhering to them. The seeds, in their parchment, are then dried in the shade, in a well-ventilated area. The moisture content of the seeds should not fall below 10 per cent, otherwise the viability will be seriously affected. The seeds should be sorted to eliminate any which are small or abnormally shaped, or are infested with pests.

A coating of charcoal dust is given to the seeds if they are to be stored for up to four months, or if transportation is planned. This coating will be supplemented by spraying or dusting with fungicides such as copper or mercuric fungicides, particularly against 'damping-off'. Preventive insecticides such as aldrin dust are also applied against termites and other predators in the soil.

Longer storage of up to one year may be achieved by mixing the seeds, still with their parchment intact, with charcoal. This mixture is placed between layers of hessian and is stored in a humid atmosphere.

The seedling
The most favourable stage of growth for transplanting the seedling depends on the time it has been growing in the nursery. This is also controlled by the climate: a plant of six to eight months of age is usually suitable for transplantation in an equatorial or sub-equatorial climate. At high altitudes, a period of one year may be necessary to obtain an arabica seedling suitable for transplanting.

The methods of raising plants from seed which are recommended most strongly are those practised in **shaded nurseries** where seedlings are sown in beds, or under shading specially erected for cultivation where the plants are grown in soil blocks or in plastic bags. There are two variations of these forms of cultivation.
- Sowing seeds in a seedbed, then planting out the seedlings into nursery beds, in plastic bags or in soil blocks;
- Sowing the seeds directly into nursery beds or plastic bags. This is a less selective method than the first, as it does not allow for examination of the seedlings on planting out, but it does cut out handling of the delicate seedlings.

The use of plastic bags or black polythene sleeves 0.05 mm thick, of standardised dimensions[1], makes it easier to transport the plant with its ball of soil. It also reduces the risk of the plant not 'taking' upon transplanting. The disadvantages in economic terms are the additional costs of the containers and the need to import into the nursery the soil required for filling the bags (approximately 3 kg per bag).

The seed-bed consists of a wooden box or part of a nursery bed to which sand and humus have been added and in which the seeds, spaced 2 cm apart and planted approximately 1 cm deep, are sown. After four

1 Diameter 12 cm, depth 35 cm for seedlings; diameter 15 cm, depth 25/27.5 cm for cuttings, both sizes to be provided with one or two rows of percolation holes in the lower third of the bag.

to six weeks the cotyledonary leaves have developed (Fig 9). This operation does not, therefore, require a large area. On the other hand, it is estimated that the area of ground needed for the nursery itself, that is, the nursery beds or blocks of plastic bags (1.2 – 1.4 m wide) and the paths between the beds (0.6 m wide to allow a wheelbarrow to pass through in addition to the main access roads (2 – 3 m wide to allow for passage of tractors and trailers) is approximately equivalent to one hundredth of the total area of land to be planted (Fig 10).

Fig 9   *Seedlings grown from selected, six week old seed (collection of the Federacion Nacional de Cafeteros de Colombia)*

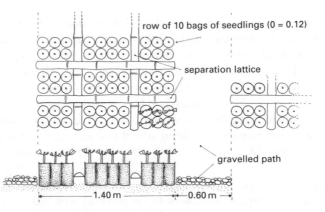

Fig 10   *Sketch of a nursery bed with plants in plastic bags*

18

The nursery area, from which all tree stumps should have been carefully removed, requires a permanent supply of water for irrigating the plants. An area with a slight gradient is preferable, but it should not be liable to flooding. The soil should have a good humus content and the nursery must be sited as close as possible to the plots in which the seedlings will be planted out.

The shading, which should be approximately 2.5 m above ground level, may be constructed economically from local materials such as stakes, bamboo and palm leaves, if only a temporary installation is required. More permanent shading requires solid and durable materials such as wooden or concrete uprights or metal tubing for supporting wires. These are covered by a wooden lattice or plastic shade netting, designed to allow the required amount of sunshine to pass through (Figs 11, 12 and 13).

Care of the seedlings

If seedlings are to be transferred from a seed-bed to a nursery bed, planting out must be done, observing the precautions usual in horticultural practice. These include firming the earth carefully after planting so as to avoid leaving air pockets around the roots. The taproot should be in a vertical position and the roots can be trimmed using secateurs or a sharp knife if necessary. The collar of the seedling should be positioned at soil level.

Maintenance involves little more than watering and weeding, the quantity of water required per day being in the order of five litres per square

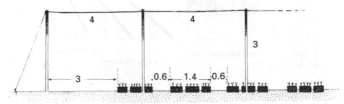

Fig 11   *Cross-section of shaded nursery*

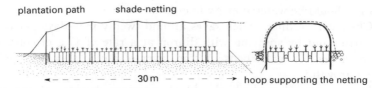

Fig 12   *Arrangement of shade-netting*

19

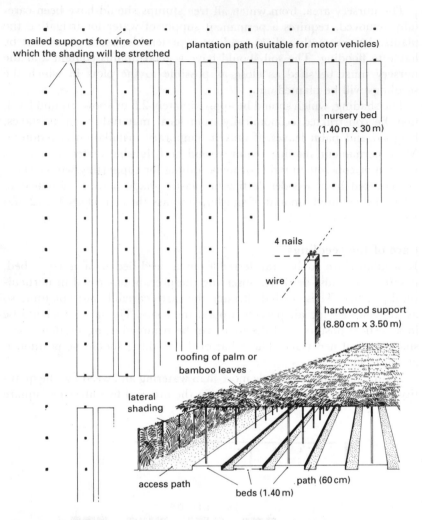

nailed supports for wire over which the shading will be stretched

plantation path (suitable for motor vehicles)

nursery bed (1.40 m x 30 m)

4 nails

wire

hardwood support (8.80 cm x 3.50 m)

roofing of palm or bamboo leaves

lateral shading

access path

path (60 cm)

beds (1.40 m)

Fig 13 *Typical layout of a nursery showing detail of part of a block*

metre. During the rainy season, the plants should be watered every time there are five consecutive days without rain. During the dry season, the plants should be watered every five days.

Chemical weeding, which saves around twenty man-days per annum, is carried out by spraying with diuron at a rate of 17 g of commercial product per 100 m² of beds. A thin layer of mulch also helps to limit weed growth.

Disease control methods should, if necessary, be carried out against 'damping-off' disease using copper-based treatments, or against *Cercospora* spp. (leaf spots) by increasing the shade. The main pests such as mole crickets, larvae and grubs, stem borers and termites will be controlled by dusting the soil with insecticides such as Aldrin (under restricted use) and organophosphates, or spraying the leaves with persistent insecticides against defoliating caterpillars such as *Epiplema* spp.

If necessary, fertiliser can be administered by spraying the leaves with urea (30 – 50 g dissolved in 10 litres of water), applying three treatments at ten-day intervals.

Towards the end of the nursery period, the shading of the beds will be reduced by opening up the lattice or removing the plastic shade netting covering the mature seedlings to 'harden off' the plants and prepare them for transplanting. They will also be subjected to rigorous selection before being transplanted.

Vegetative propagation

Multiplication by vegetative means (mainly cuttings) enables the total reproduction of all the characteristics of a selected individual plant, for instance production capacity, reaction to environment (soil, climate, the risks of attacks by pests) and the technological and organoleptic properties of commercial coffee.

Vegetative propagation involves the use of cuttings, budwood, scion wood for grafting and layering, taken from marked trees; these are sometimes grown specially for this purpose as mother-plant trees in a cutting-producing nursery. A plantation grown from these trees will then be made up of clones or clonal mixtures, an indispensable combination where self-sterile coffee plants such as the robusta types are grown (cross pollination can result in variation in plant characteristics). Earlier maturity, together with a considerable increase in productivity is therefore achieved from vegetatively propagated plants when compared with seedlings.

Propagation by cuttings
This is the most commonly used form of vegetative propagation. It has now been perfected and can be undertaken almost on an industrial scale. Internodes of orthotropic suckers (the plagiotropic branches only reproduce bushes growing horizontally) are taken from selected clones and grown in special cutting-producing nurseries. This intensive production system presupposes that the parent clones have previously been selected according to their suitability for producing cuttings. The robustas appear to be better suited for this purpose than the arabicas, which themselves are more suitable than the *Liberio-excelsoides* hybrids. The internodal sections which are used as cuttings develop their roots in a porous substrate in propagators (boxes) or specially prepared cutting

trenches. The rooted cuttings are then planted out in plastic bags, hardened off under shade and in a humid environment, then cultivated for six to eight months under conventional shading before being transplanted.

The cutting-producing nursery should be sited on a plot which has been prepared very thoroughly, with the ground cleared of tree stumps and the soil broken up. It will contain 18 000 rooted cuttings per hectare, according to the planting plan outlined in Fig 14.

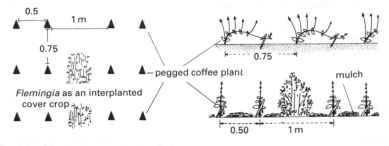

Fig 14   *Planting in a cutting-producing nursery*

The natural habit of the coffee plant encourages the rapid development of orthotropic shoots. These may also be induced by bending the main branches to encourage the growth of upright suckers. An abundant mulch such as cut grasses, compost, together with the parchment or outer husks of the coffee beans, should be applied to inhibit weed growth and keep the ground moist by reducing evaporation.

Maintenance consists of removing all vegetation which does not produce useful propagation material, and bending the lateral branches to encourage the development of orthotropic suckers, replacing these with new branches when the maximum number of suckers has been produced from the axillary buds.

A supply of nitrogenous fertiliser of 100 g per plant is recommended in four applications, that is 25 g of urea after each removal of cuttings and an application during the dormant period in the cool, dry season. In the event of the development of bronze chlorosis in the older leaves, an application of magnesium sulphate as a spray is recommended.

The cutting-producing nursery can be used after the plants have been growing for six to nine months. Full production may be achieved for robusta after fifteen to eighteen months, and this corresponds to the annual production of 150 – 200 cuttings per plant, that is 2.7 million – 3.6 million cuttings per hectare per year.

Cuttings are taken from a plant in the cutting-producing nursery at intervals of three months. Rotation must be arranged in order to keep the propagators regularly supplied. The cuttings are taken in the morning and, if preparation and insertion is to be postponed, they should be kept in polythene bags in a cool, shaded place.

Selection and preparation of the cuttings

This phase includes the removal, using a grafting knife, of the green to semi-ripened branches, which are produced from orthotropic suckers which have developed six to eight nodes. These suckers should have their tips removed fifteen days before the cuttings are taken. The branches are cut into short segments 7 – 10 cm in length, consisting of one node and two leaves which are cut half or a third of the way along their length so as to limit evapotranspiration. One method of differentiating between the various clones of *C. Canephora* used in the mixture to be planted, is to cut the leaves into different shapes, as indicated in Fig 16. The upper portion of the cutting must be cut as close as possible to the axils of the leaves in order to prevent further development of the primary extra-axillary buds which are situated 0.5 – 1 cm from the axil (Fig 15).

The cuttings may then be cleaved, that is they are cut into two longitudinal segments, each having one leaf. This operation is only possible, however, if the cuttings are sufficiently large in diameter (Fig 15).

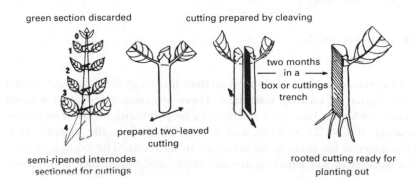

Fig 15   *Preparation of the cuttings*

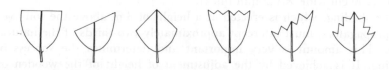

Fig 16   *Examples of various types of cuts made to leaves to assist in recognition of the origin of clonal cuttings*

23

Propagators

These are conventional **cutting boxes**, made of cemented breeze blocks, with compartment dimensions of 120 × 120 cm covered by a wooden lattice supporting a sheet of polythene film. In the bottom of each box, alternate layers of stones and gravel facilitate drainage beneath the rooting medium. This consists of a layer of chemically inert, porous material which is at least 20 cm thick. It may be a mixture of coarse, fermented wood shavings which have been screened and washed, coarse-grained river sand, rice husks or the parchment or composted outer skins of coffee. This substrate should be sterilised once a year by heating, using steam or by applying chloropicrin, to prevent infestation by nematodes or bacteria (Fig 17).

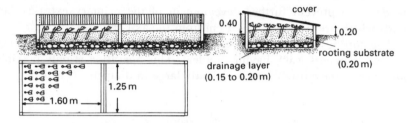

Fig 17   *Cuttings trench*

An effective and less costly method than the use of the cemented cutting boxes is that of **cutting trenches**. These are constituted from wooden planks, without a base, and are covered by polythene sheets. The planks measure 400 × 20 × 2 cm, and are half buried in the ground. It is advantageous for them to be arranged in batteries. The bottom of each box consists of soil which is already there, and which has simply been loosened.

It is important that the upper surface of the substrate used, which is similar to that already described for cutting boxes, is relatively close to the cover of the boxes, but care must be taken to ensure that the cuttings do not come into contact with the plastic. The trenches are hermetically sealed by a wooden framework supporting a sheet of translucent polythene (130 cm wide × 0.2 mm thick).

The shading, which is erected at a height of 3 m above the soil over the propagators, must intercept approximately two thirds of the natural light. This amount is very important and determines the success of rooting. It is achieved by the adjustment of height of the wooden or bamboo lattice shading used, and by taking care to position the shading in a north-south direction. It should be supplemented by lateral shading consisting of a living hedge or plastic trellis grown or placed around the battery of boxes (Fig 13).

How the operation progresses

The prepared cuttings are inserted vertically, in parallel rows, into the previously moistened substrate to a depth at which the stalk of the leaf just touches the sawdust which partly covers it. This arrangement is essential if leaf drop, which would be an indication that the plant has not taken root, is to be avoided. The correct planting density is between 400 and 500 cuttings per square metre (Fig 17). When one compartment of the propagator is full, it is sprayed with water and the cover is carefully placed over it.

Each morning, the cuttings should be moistened by applying a fine mist of 0.5 l water per 1000 cuttings. Spraying should be discontinued as soon as the micro-droplets deposited on the leaves start to join together and form droplets. The objective of this spraying is not only to maintain the humidity of the environment, but also to stabilise the temperature inside the box at a level of between 25 and 30°C. In the dry season, a second spraying should be carried out in the afternoon.

After twenty days, the scar callus will have developed, and the first roots will then begin to appear. The rooted cuttings may be transferred after six to eight weeks of growth, with all the cuttings being removed after a period of three months. Any cuttings which have not produced roots by this time may be discarded and the propagator prepared for the following batch (Fig 18).

If there are no adverse conditions, the success rates vary according to the clone or stock and the physiological condition of the prepared cuttings. There is normally a 60 per cent rate of rooting after eight weeks, rising to 80 per cent after twelve weeks. In relatively difficult climates, due to the variation in the environment, an average yield of 50 per cent can be expected. A lower yield may be due to one or more serious deficiencies in the environment in which the cuttings are grown, the preparation and the insertion of the cuttings or in the way they are maintained. These problems must be analysed and eliminated if yields are to be improved.

Planting out and hardening off

The rooted cuttings are then planted into black polythene bags containing enriched, standard nursery soil (one part natural clay loam soil, one part sand/fertile topsoil and one part manure or compost). The black polythene bags are 0.05 mm thick, with expanding sides and perforations in the lower half. The size of the bags should be 15 cm in diameter and 25 – 27.5 cm in depth; they are filled almost to the top with compost and are well watered.

The cuttings are planted up to about half of their lengths, using a

Fig 18   *Rooted cuttings taken from a propagator*

Fig 19   *Arrangement of boxes for hardening off and planting out the rooted cuttings. RCA – Boukoko Station (PUJOL collection)*

26

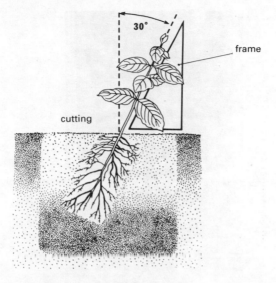

Fig 20   *Oblique planting with a frame*

dibber. The roots, shortened to 7 cm if necessary, are spread out evenly, taking care not to damage or twist them. The earth is then firmed, using the fingers and the plants are placed under standard shading to become established (50 per cent light and lateral shading). The bags are arranged in beds 140 cm wide, which are separated by alleys 60 cm wide (Fig 19).

The plants should be well spaced out to allow adequate room for growth, particularly if they are to remain in situ for more than six to eight months.

During the first three weeks, the young plants are allowed to become acclimatised or 'hardened off' under a plastic tunnel. This is the period during which the root system of the cutting becomes established and is far more likely to take place without losses in a humid and confined atmosphere, under shading similar to that described for use in the propagators (Fig 17). In the absence of a plastic tunnel, a favourable environment can be achieved by erecting a layer of double shading just above the cuttings. This arrangement is liable to lead to transpiration losses and frequent sprayings will be required during the first three weeks of the acclimatisation period to maintain a humid atmosphere, in contrast to the plastic tunnel method of protection. After hardening off, the cuttings are uncovered and are treated in exactly the same way as described for the seedlings throughout their growing period.

Modern methods of growing vegetative organs and tissues now enable the intensive **in-vitro** production of **micro-cuttings** of coffee plants to be undertaken (Fig 21). Commercial systems of raising horticultural

Fig 21 *Arabusta plantlet from a somatic embryo pricked out on rooting medium (in-vitro plant) (DUBLIN collection)*

cuttings makes possible the transportation of cutting material, prepared cuttings and/or rooted cuttings, over a limited time span (from four to eight days). This material is generally placed in bundles in sealed polythene bags, in a non-sterile environment, with humidity enriched by the addition of moss, and often without a health guarantee if fungicidal and insecticidal treatments are not carefully applied. The use of in-vitro micro-cuttings enables propagation material to be dispatched free from germs and viruses, in sealed glass or plastic containers. These may be transported without difficulty across the borders of coffee-growing countries throughout the world.

Rooted micro-cuttings (in-vitro plants) also require a phase of horticultural acclimatisation, followed by careful raising, during which the root and shoot systems will develop into those of a normal plant.

Grafting

This procedure originated in the clonal plantations created at the beginning of the 20th century by Dutch farmers in Java. Sterile plants, produced from single clones of robusta (monoclonal), were the reason for the study of the self-incompatibility of the coffee plants of the canephora species.

Grafting is currently used in Central America in controlling nematodes, where a nematode-susceptible variety of arabica is grafted onto canephora coffee plants, having resistant or tolerant root systems. This technique, however, now plays a secondary role in the propagation of cloned coffee plants following the establishment of propagation by cuttings on a commercial scale.

The techniques used in grafting are very traditional: cleft grafting, grafting by approach and shield grafting. The problems associated with this method of propagation, which make it now less popular, stem from the affinities and incompatibilities of the varieties of species present and the level of professional skill of the operators.

Layering

This technique ensures that the layered coffee plants take well, but it is difficult and costly to carry out, involving ringing of the stem, the possible application of hormones, maintenance of a moist substrate under a plastic sleeve and establishment time. It is for these reasons that this method is really only feasible for special uses, such as research, botanical investigations, etc.

> *Vegetative propagation is the basis of the establishment of clonal plantations, making both cultivation and harvesting easier and ensuring a good biological standardisation of the product.*

2.2 Planting coffee plants

Transplanting the young plants to their permanent positions in the plots is preceded by operations which are related to the perennial nature of the crop and the various treatments which will be applied. These are the selection and marking out of the plots, soil preparation, choice of layout and density of planting and the technical operations involved in transplanting.

Selection and marking out of the plots

In small plantations, the size and shape of the area to be cultivated are generally determined by social factors, for example a family inheritance, tribal customs, private letting, etc. Also relevant is the legal status of the

29

farmer; whether owner, usufructuary, tenant farmer or share-cropper, etc., and/or that of the land, for instance land title deed, common law or amicable agreement. These constraints are generally less important for the larger plantations, but the design of the plots may then be limited by topographical (relief and altitude) or soil-type restrictions, e.g. level of fertility, the presence of marshy areas, a lateric hard pan, gravelly areas or a sub-soil layer which is less than 1.2 m deep (this being the minimum depth for the development of the taproot of the coffee plant and for moisture retention in the dry season).

Selection of the plots to be established is therefore preceded by ecological, social, family, economic and financial considerations. They lead to the selection of the production system, whether it be a family concern, a small-scale or commercial business. This is dependent on the size of the area to be farmed (from 0 – 5 hectares, 5 – 30 hectares or more than 30 hectares). Thus, it will be necessary for farmers to adopt the intensive method as soon as a certain level of land saturation is exceeded in a given region, whereas the extensive method will be more suitable for coffee plantations on large, still unoccupied areas, even in a family concern.

From the technical point of view, these observations indicate that the plantation should be sited:
● Close to the centre of activity of the plantation, be this either the planter's residence (for regular supervision) or the place where the crops are processed and stored. It may sometimes even be the area where the nursery is located;
● Depending on the topography (degree of slope) or the availability of water and possibilities for irrigation.

In general, the plots which are to be planted are located as near as possible to the working area, that is transport and delivery of new plants and removal of harvested crop. These considerations are also related to the choice of the size and shape of the plots. It is considered that unit plots of two to five hectares and up to ten hectares (200 × 500 m for very large plantations with grassed over access paths and roads) are the most profitable.

When a plantation is very large, for instance a group of communities, a state plantation or private companies, a surveyor is required to mark out, delimit and plan various components of the plantation.

Land preparation

Methods used for clearing the marked out plots vary, depending mainly on the nature of the vegetation covering them (forest or savannah with trees) and involve techniques which are traditional to all plantations of tropical crops.

In **forest areas**, the following operations are carried out:

- **Felling** involves two stages, first the undergrowth, then the wood of trees more than 20 cm in diameter. The chain-saw is used, although large tracked vehicles or 'treedozers' are, unfortunately, still required for more extensive areas populated by large, hard-wooded trees. To counteract the risk of root rot, it is recommended that the largest trees, which cannot be uprooted, be poisoned beforehand so that the stumps die. Felling covers the land area with a mass of cut vegetation, which has to be removed after a short drying out period. Continuous small fires are used to burn leaves and small branches;

- **Chain-sawing** reduces the felled trees to sections which are easier to remove;

- **Removal of the timber** consists, principally, of removing the trunks nearest to the edges of the plot using a type of winch and of lining up the lightest wood debris in the proposed inter-rows. The heavier logs which are some distance from the roads, are piled up in long rows or swaths. This operation, known as **swathing**, is carried out by hand, using tools or levers to avoid the top layer of the soil being scraped by tracked vehicles. It is concentrated in every two or three inter-rows, depending on the quantity of wood to be removed and the possibility of intercropping (food crops or cover plants) requiring clean ground. Before swathing is carried out, it is essential that there is a layout plan, which includes a brief outline of the planting rows (Figs 22 – 25).

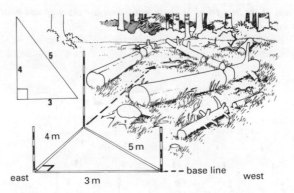

Fig 22   *Sketch of the first right-angled triangle marked out with the aid of three poles with the dimensions given*

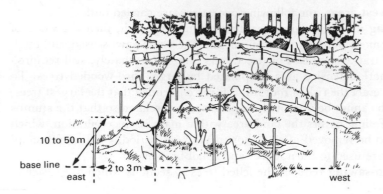

Fig 23   *Marking out, every 10 to 50 m, of rows perpendicular to the planned inter-row spacing*

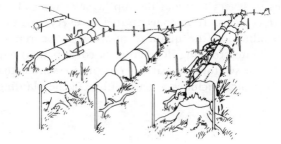

Fig 24   *Removal of the trees felled by chain saw; these are sawn up and positioned in every second or third inter-row*

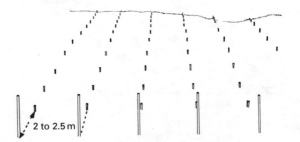

Fig 25   *Staking out the rows at the selected distances between each row in preparation for planting*

32

In **savannah areas**, felling, sawing up and removal of the few trees which exist is carried out without burning, in order to preserve the reserve of humus in the soil as much as possible. These procedures are followed, one month later, by removal of any new growth and hoeing or ploughing the soil to a depth of 0.15 m. A second and final hoeing or cross-ploughing takes place after a further month. Seeds or seedlings of a cover crop are then sown or planted out in the loosened soil. Suitable crops include *Pueraria, Desmodium, Mimosa invisa* or *Flemingia*. Temporary shade plants, such as Angol peas or 'seedless' *Leucaena*, may also be planted.

Choice of layout and density of planting

This is dependent on the various socio-economic factors already referred to, but these two parameters depend above all on the species and/or variety of coffee which is to be grown.

Layout
One basic principle of layout, is that planting in rows will subsequently make cultivation and harvesting easier. The following systems are therefore possible, depending on the gradients of the plots: square planting, triangular planting, in alternate rows (square with rows staggered by a half-length between plants), in hedges on fairly flat land (with a slope of less than 5 per cent), and on contour lines and individual terraces on sloping ground.

The usual densities
Canephora: from 1000 to 2000 trees/hectare, depending on planting distances as follows:
 4.0 × 2.5 m (1100 trees/hectare) – allows for mechanisation of the inter-row;
 3.0 × 3.0 m (1100 trees/hectare) – previously a standard planting density;
 3.0 × 2.5 m (1330 trees/hectare) – intermediate planting density for robusta;
 3.0 × 2.0 m (1660 trees/hectare) – intermediate planting density for robusta;
 3.0 × 1.7 m (1960 trees/hectare) – high density, a new standard planting density for robusta;
 2.5 × 2.0 m (2000 trees/hectare) – high density planting.
Arabica: from 1000 to 2500 trees/hectare for typica, bourbon and mundo novo varieties, depending on planting distances as follows:
 4.0 × 2.5 m (1000 trees/hectare) – a former Brazilian standard with intercropping. Mechanisation of the inter-row and/or of the crops is possible;

3.0 × 3.0 m approx. (1100 trees/hectare) – a former East African standard of 10 feet by 10 feet;
2.74 m × 2.74 m (1329 trees/hectare) – a recently common East African standard;
2.74 m × 1.37 m (2658 trees/hectare) – a recently common East African standard;
2.0 × 2.0 m (2500 trees/hectare).
From 2500 to 10 000 trees/hectare for the dwarf varieties **ruiru 11**, **caturra**, **catuai** and **colombia**, depending on planting distances as follows:
2.0 × 2.0 m (2500 trees/hectare);
2.0 × 1.5 m (3300 trees/hectare);
2.0 × 1.0 m (5300 trees/hectare);
1.0 × 1.0 m (10 000 trees/hectare).

High density planting for arabica, of more than 5000 plants per hectare, requires a considerable investment in terms of plants, fertilisers and treatments, etc. and the strict application of very carefully planned procedures. It is therefore only practised on large plantations in Latin America.

The density of planting also varies considerably, depending on the pruning system adopted. Experiments have shown that a certain degree of flexibility is permissible for spacing and that, in order to improve productivity and production at an early stage, it is important to have 5000 – 7000 stems with productive branches per hectare. Thus, in a multiple-stem system, 2000 trees per hectare, each with three stems, would be expected to give similar yields to lower densities (1000 to 1300 trees per hectare) with a higher number of stems (four to five) per plant.

In order to make maintenance easier, or to facilitate interplanting with a temporary food crop or cover plant, spacing of around three metres between the rows is recommended for robusta plants. For arabica coffee, a traditional method in Brazil is to define the density by the number of planting holes per hectare, but the practice is to transplant or sow several coffee plants per hole, that is two to three, 30 cm apart, which multiplies the number of productive stems per hectare. Despite the inconvenience this presents for maintaining these multiple and permanent stems, this system offers the advantage of increased mutual protection, particularly with regard to resistance to wind. For this reason it is a recommended practice in Zimbabwe, where the disease of the trunks caused by a *Fusarium* species is widespread.

The selection of the most favourable spacing is always a compromise between high densities with the need, if high productivity is to be achieved, for maximum light, and traditional spacing which meets this requirement and also allows easy access for maintenance and harvesting.

As far as the exposure of the bushes to maximum sunlight is concerned, it is recommended that the rows are planted facing north to south.

Technical operations involved in planting

Staking out

Stakes made of brushwood, pieces of bamboo, etc. are used to mark the planting positions in accordance with the distances selected. The basic alignment generally follows the direction of the largest access path or road at the edge of the plot which should preferably run in an east-west direction. A surveying chain or measuring poles, cut to the correct dimensions, can be used to measure distances and enable the perpendicular base lines (sides of a right-angled triangle: 3 m × 4 m × 5 m) to be drawn (Fig 22). A mason's level and a stand will be helpful in drawing the contours on sloping ground.

Planting holes

The dimensions of planting holes will vary, depending on the fertility and compactness of the ground. They should be 0.3 – 0.9 m deep and have an average capacity of 0.4 cubic metres. They should be dug two to four weeks before transplanting and should be filled in again a few days beforehand, thoroughly mixing the soil. This aerates the soil and stimulates biological activity, particularly if fertiliser has been added to the bottom of the hole such as manure, compost, phosphate or fertilisers containing potassium and phosphate. Addition of an insecticide to the refilling mixture helps to control soil-born insect pests. Equipment required includes spades, hoes or digging forks. In mechanised operations a mechanical auger, possibly power-driven and carried on a tractor, can be used for excavating the holes.

Transplanting

This is a simple operation, commonly used in arboriculture, which is made easier by using plants which have been grown in plastic bags. The age of the plant may vary from six to eight months in hot areas, and from twelve to eighteen months in cool areas (arabica). The roots have to be trimmed to prevent the taproots from becoming twisted, by cutting the plastic bag with a knife 1 cm from the bottom. Secateurs may be used if the plant has bare roots, and some of the foliage may have to be trimmed also using secateurs, to reduce transpiration during the rooting phase of the plant. The choice of system used is dictated by the availability of transport facilities for supplying the plants and the size of the area to be planted daily.

Transplanting with **bare roots** is the most economical method. With little weight to transport, the plants can be chosen according to the quality of the root system, but extra care must be taken when uprooting, transporting and storing the plant, which must be kept shaded, under damp sackcloth; and in planting using a dibber. Above all it is uncertain whether the plant will take in the prevailing climatic conditions.

Transplanting in a **root ball**, with or without a 'Java' dibber to lift the plant from the beds, retaining the soil in compressed balls around the roots ensures minimum disturbance of the root system. The plant will almost certainly take if the ball is compact and the collar is placed at the right level, with the soil well firmed around the foot of the plant. The plants are sometimes grown in plastic bags or other containers (page 26 and Fig 9), reducing losses during transplanting even further.

These methods are relatively costly because of the volume of earth transported with the plants and the fact that they can only be selected on the basis of the appearance of their shoot systems. If plastic bags are used, workers must remember to remove them when planting, since they are not biodegradable, otherwise development will be inhibited.

Timing of transplanting is an important consideration. It should be as early as possible, once the rainy season is well established and the soil is sufficiently moist, having received approximately 150 mm of rain. Appropriate months are March, April or May in latitudes north of the equator and September, October or November, south of the Equator.

> *Planting by the bare root method is recommended, provided that this is carried out with care and that the plant is well-positioned in the hole, with the soil being sufficiently firmed around the roots to prevent air pockets, etc.*

Any planting of temporary or permanent shade trees should be completed before the coffee plants are transplanted, in order to limit competition between the root systems. An example of competition has been demonstrated by the leaves of coffee plants becoming yellow when they are planted at the same time as the roots of a cover crop such as *Flemingia congesta* are developing. *Flemingia* is an excellent upright cover plant and/or wind-break which later develops a deep root system.

> *When planting out, do not forget to remove the plastic bag, which, unless it is biodegradable, will severely hinder root development.*

After planting out, each plant should be sheltered by a covering of leaves such as palm fronds. Mulching and, if necessary, irrigation should also be carried out in the event of drought. After a few weeks, a count should be made of the dead plants which will have to be replaced either before the end of the rainy season, or during the following humid season in a climate with four seasons. As a general rule, no more than 5 per cent of the plants should have to be replaced.

3 Maintaining the coffee plantation

3.1 The environment of the plant and plantation

The coffee plantation has to be maintained in excellent condition if the plants are to develop vegetatively, become mature, flower and bear fruit under the best conditions.

Controlling the environment

Assuming that the bushes have been planted in such a way as to limit soil erosion, the following maintenance procedures will be required:

Controlling competition from weeds

This requires soil cultivation methods which may be deep or superficial and intensive or extensive, depending on the nature of the types of weed which occur and the method of cultivation used.

Many of the most common weeds, which compete for nutrient and water resources, belong to the family Gramineae, for example *Paspalum*, *Imperata*, *Setaria*, *Agropyrum*, etc. There are also many hardy, broad-leaved weeds which should be removed when they grow beyond a certain point and, in any event, before they flower.

The cutting or uprooting of these weeds can be mechanised using a rotary cutter, disc cultivator, rotovator or mechanical hoeing machine, these being powered by a 4-wheel tractor, a single-axle tractor or draught animals, depending on the type of machinery used. However, such work is often done manually on small plantations or in areas where labour is plentiful, using machetes or various types of hoe (Fig 26).

Effective eradication requires repeated weeding, sometimes every month in the rainy season, and at least four to six times a year in order to keep the weeds under adequate control.

Mechanical weeding, using a rotary cutter or similar equipment, is rapid and does not damage the top soil, but a disadvantage is that it

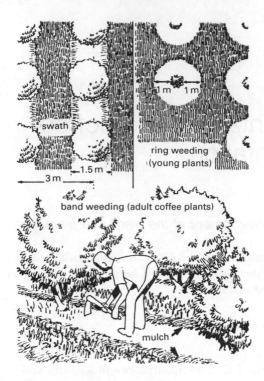

Fig 26 *Manual weeding*

encourages multiplication of graminaceous weeds, competition from which is only reduced for a very short time.

In order to minimise these disadvantages, the use of mechanised and/or manually operated equipment should be restricted to the critical areas, such as the rows between the coffee plants. This can be achieved by **band weeding** from one end to the other, along the line of coffee plants. **Ring weeding**, removing weeds growing around the foot of the plants, is a manual operation (Fig 26). Weeds can also be controlled by establishing a cover crop or mulching between the plants.

The current trend is towards increasing use of **herbicides**, often, on recently planted coffee plantations, in combination with the installation of a black plastic sheet 40 – 65 cm wide along the row. This serves to minimise any damage which may be caused by the herbicide drifting onto the young plants.

The herbicides used in coffee growing may act upon contact, systemically or residually by translocation. Normally, the treatments are used at the pre- or post-emergence stages of weed growth. Although there are definite advantages to be gained from the use of herbicides, they are, however, subject to certain restrictions:

- They require a specialised workforce with a technical knowledge of weed characteristics, the products being used, equipment and field use, and also an understanding of the characteristics of the soil and the environment;
- If used incorrectly they may be harmful to the coffee plant or its environment, also dangerous to the operator who should follow safety regulations closely.

> *The instructions issued by the manufacturers of herbicides and the advice given by experimental centres must be strictly adhered to.*

Treatment is generally carried out in two stages as the weeds begin to develop, with an interval of two, or even three weeks between applications. The product is applied using spraying equipment. Manual sprayers are sufficient to cover an area containing 800 to 1000 trees in a day, whereas tractor drawn sprayers are used where 8000 to 10 000 trees have to be sprayed per day. The herbicide is contained in bottles with a protective shield fitted around the T-jets, to prevent the herbicide from drifting onto the sensitive parts of the shrubs. This is particularly important when non-selective products are used and also in windy weather.

The following herbicides are recommended:

- **2,4-D amine**: 1.5 – 3.5 kg ai/ha (active ingredient per hectare); it has a total and systemic action at the post- and pre-emergence stages;
- **Dalapon**: 5 – 10 kg ai/ha; a systemic herbicide, applied at the post-emergence stage, it can be used for general or localised spraying;
- **Paraquat**: 1.5 – 3 l ai/ha; used as a general spray, acts on contact (treatments to be repeated at each regrowth), applied at the post-emergence stage;
- **Glyphosate**: 2 – 4 l ai/ha; a systemic herbicide, applied at post-emergence stage; is more effective in controlling regrowth of weeds after a previous cutting back, by hand or machine;
- **Diuron**: 2 – 4 l ai/ha; general in action, applied at pre-emergence stage; is very effective for weed control in the nursery;
- **Basta**: 2 – 3 l ai/ha; a general spray, acts on contact. Apply at post-emergence stage;
- **Fusilade**: 2 – 4 l ai/ha; a grass selective spray. Apply at post-emergence stage.
- **Gallant**: 3 – 4 l ai/ha; a grass selective. Apply at post-emergence stage.

Depending on the type of chemical used, most herbicides are diluted with 300 to 500 l of water per hectare, mixed with a **surfactant** (surface active agent) when leaf application is involved.

Low volume sprays are possible (approximately 100 l of water) with low volume nozzles, thereby reducing the amount of herbicide required, e.g. 0.5 – 1.0 l ai/ha of glyphosate on annual weeds.

> *Great care must be taken to prepare the herbicidal solutions in relation to the areas to be treated in a single day; it is most important to reserve the spraying equipment exclusively for this purpose and to wash it carefully with water and detergent after use, keeping well clear of water sources used by people and animals.*

The application of fertilisers

The fertility and correct structure of the soil can be maintained by careful use of mineral and organic fertilisers with particular attention being given to the rate, timing and frequency of application.

The objective in using mineral fertilisers (see next chapter) is to meet the specific nutritional needs of the coffee plant. These will vary, depending on the stage of growth and the annual rate of development of the coffee crop.

Irrigation

This is intended to supplement or take the place of rainfall and thus maintain the water-holding capacity of the soil at critical stages in the development of the plant, e.g. the production of new vegetative growth after planting, at flowering, during the first stages in the formation of the fruit and during fruit development.

The ways in which the coffee plants are irrigated depend above all on the topographical and edaphic features of the plantation including clay and sand content, porosity and field capacity. The method used also depends on the amount of water available, whether it is running or underground water, on the capital to be invested and the seasonal needs of the coffee plant. This may be 3 – 5 mm per day, depending on the ambient temperature. A study of these irrigation requirements will serve as a guide in drawing up the water supply programme: the rate and frequency of application (ideally 150 mm per month where the rainfall is inadequate, with a minimum threshold application of 30 mm, particularly in sandy, clay soils.

In coffee growing, a distinction is made between:
- **Surface irrigation**: in a furrow or channel. The application of this system requires a carefully drawn plan of the topography of the area. Furrow irrigation is relatively difficult to monitor and may result in a great deal of water being wasted. There is also a serious risk of erosion;
- **Overhead sprinkler irrigation**: a relatively expensive investment involving motorised pumps, hoses and sprinklers. This is also a fairly demanding, labour-intensive operation since it involves moving the

hoses and sprinklers. It does, however, enable the plants to be irrigated in a fairly natural way and is fairly flexible, since it is almost independent of the topography. It could, however, be criticised for promoting the spread of diseases such as rusts, due to the humid environment it creates. On the other hand, it enables fertilisers or leaf-spray pesticides to be applied at the same time;

- **Drip irrigation**: this would appear to be the most suitable method for meeting the needs of the plants, since it supplies a regular amount of water to the root systems. It is also the most economic system in terms of water use, and is relatively easy to install, but it is expensive in investment terms, involving a pumping station, purification tanks, distribution network of plastic hoses and the provision of drip nozzles normally based on a one to one plant requirement. It is approximately six to ten times more expensive than the overhead sprinkler equipment.

Whatever method is chosen, the main conclusion to be drawn is that the irrigation of coffee plantations is particularly profitable in marginal coffee-growing areas where it enables normal growth and production to occur. A major advantage is that, with irrigation, fertilisers can be used to their maximum effect.

Routine cultivations

Apart from the application of fertilisers and the use of irrigation, both of which make a considerable contribution to the health and vigour of coffee plants, the following techniques are also necessary:

Pruning
This procedure forms a major part of the management of a coffee plantation. It is carried out for various reasons, the most important being to shape the tree so as to make the most of the productive wood in the space available. Pruning is also carried out to remove old and diseased wood, to remove non-productive suckers, to facilitate harvesting of the fruit by promoting fruiting on easily accessible branches, and to rejuvenate plants which have been neglected. Details of pruning techniques are described in section 3.2.

Health inspection of the shrubs
Regular checks should be made to ascertain whether the trees are in good health and whether there is any damage from diseases and/or insects. Any phytosanitary precautions taken against pests and insects should preferably be carried out with just consideration given to the natural biological balance, and appropriate pesticides only used when the level of damage extends beyond economic thresholds. The main predators of

coffee, their risks to plant health, disease symptoms and ways in which both pests and disease can be controlled are the subject of Chapter five.

Maintenance of shade trees and windbreaks

When permanent shading or windbreak rows have become established, the trees or shrubs providing the windbreak must be maintained since, if they are neglected, they are likely to be ineffective and may even damage the coffee plants by producing excessive shade, competing with the coffee for water and soil nutrients, or providing a habitat for parasites, etc.

For this reason they should be periodically pruned, thereby limiting the extent to which they compete with the coffee plants. The debris remaining after this pruning can also provide a useful mulch for application between the coffee rows.

Fertiliser must also be applied to windbreak trees, particularly when they are growing on poor, sandy soils. They should be inspected regularly and, if necessary, treated to restore them to full vigour.

Replacement of dead coffee trees

A certain number of trees will wither and die each year, at a rate varying from two to five per cent. They must be replaced but it is also necessary to establish the cause of death, such as climatic conditions, diseases, etc. If they die due to poor cultural techniques, the reason will be obvious and can be rectified. However, if they die due to infertile soil conditions, the areas involved should be abandoned in order to avoid further non-productive expenditure.

3.2 *Pruning*

Purpose

When it begins to bear fruit, the young coffee plant is structurally and functionally symmetrical, with regularly arranged branches one above the other in tiers, from the base of the plant to the top (Fig 27). Flowers and fruits in varying numbers, depending on the species, the production system and the environment, occupy the older fruiting branches. The reproductive surface therefore increases as the tree develops new branches. These extend in a centrifugal arrangement for three to four years and sometimes branch to produce secondary or tertiary structures. Represented graphically, this surface increases rapidly in size for five to seven years, accompanied by the flowering phase. The plant then passes through an optimum growth stage and, finally, gradually decreases in vigour, the rate depending on the physiological constitution of the plant and its environment.

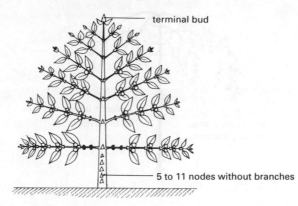

terminal bud

5 to 11 nodes without branches

Fig 27   *Diagram of the structure of a young coffee plant*

If allowed to grow freely without pruning, the symmetry of the young plant gradually becomes distorted as follows:

- The stem (or stems in the case of naturally multiple-stemmed varieties) can sometimes grow to a considerable height (from five to fifteen metres) depending on the species or variety. This results in the production of a cluster of young fruit-bearing branches, some distance from the ground;
- The branches become longer, losing their basal leaves after fruiting, and retaining only a small number of leaves or productive secondary branches at their tips;
- In the central part of the tree, the branches which have lost their leaves begin to dry out and die, leaving only a short stump or a scar on the trunk and a mass of non-productive suckers (Fig 28).

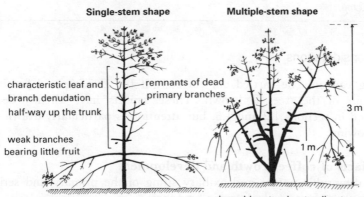

Single-stem shape   Multiple-stem shape

characteristic leaf and
branch denudation
half-way up the trunk

remnants of dead
primary branches

3 m

weak branches
bearing little fruit

1 m

branchless trunk extending to more
than one metre from the ground

Fig 28   *Coffee plants growing freely*

43

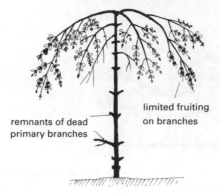

limited fruiting
on branches

remnants of dead
primary branches

Fig 29   *Old capped coffee tree*

For reasons of convenience, the terminal branch is often pruned during harvesting. This accelerates the process of decline and the trunk rapidly loses its branches (Fig 29).

The purpose of pruning the coffee tree is, therefore, to restore the effective area of branches and leaf-bearing nodes as much as possible. The new branches will then be capable of producing additional inflorescence and are likely to ensure the continued development of the plant without any physiological problems such as 'die-back'. Furthermore, pruning will provide the trees with a robust and well-balanced framework which will support the fruit-bearing branches and will be at a convenient height for handling and harvesting.

> *It is essential to prune the coffee tree to ensure that the tree has a well developed fruit-bearing framework and is robust, balanced and capable of producing a good crop.*

Prior considerations

Pruning can only be carried out correctly if the growing and fruiting behaviour of the trees is known. These aspects have already been described in sections 1.2 and 1.3, but attention is particularly drawn to the following:

Basic facts of coffee growth and development
a) the dimorphic nature and axillary siting of the primary and serial buds on the stem and plagiotropic branches;
b) the siting of the vegetative shoots: plagiotropic branches develop from the topmost bud of orthotropic stems whilst lower buds remain dormant

44

or produce more orthotropic stems; secondary development of the plagiotropic branches to the detriment of inflorescence development; hormone-
induced vegetative budding of the serial buds at the nodes of the main
orthotropic stem for the production of replacement orthotropic shoots;
c) the development of the fruit-bearing branches: the initiation of the
inflorescence buds in the axils of the leaf nodes created during the preced-
ing rainy season in both arabica and canephora. Neither of these flower
again on the nodes, having exhausted their stock of axillary buds; there
is no possibility of regenerating them after defoliation.

The physiology of growth and fruiting in brief

Both physiology and growth are determined by the genetic constitution
of the species and by the periodic fluctuations of the carbohydrate/nitro-
gen (C/N) ratio. The levels of the N factor and the mineral supply
alternate at the beginning of the dry season. This is often linked with a
temporary increase in levels of the C factor (sugars), which coincides
with floral initiation.

Intervention at any stage in the plant's growth which affects the growth
of the root or shoot system, such as infestation by pests or diseases, also
contributes to a change in the hormone and nutrient balance within the
plant. This may affect the vigour and rate of development of the plant.

The choice of a pruning system involves consideration, not only of the
reaction of a single bush, but the cumulative effects on the plants throughout an entire plot of the plantation. Their arrangement within the plot,
the planting density and spacing between the rows and between plants
in the row must, therefore, be taken into account insofar as it affects the
growth reactions of the plants.

Other economic or professional considerations, such as the availability,
cost and qualifications of a skilled workforce, the possibility of the mechanisation of the pruning operation, plant protection procedures and harvesting, should also be considered when choosing the most suitable pruning method for the plantation.

The pruning systems in coffee growing

Three main methods can be used: single-stem pruning, multiple-stem
pruning and natural growth with periodical, accelerated rejuvenation.

Single-stem pruning

The object of this method is to shape a permanent framework in the form
of a single stem of moderate height, with the aim of producing fruit on
renewed secondary branches (Fig 30).

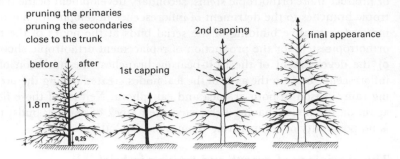

Fig 30   *Single-stem pruning*

Formative phase
This phase, which starts towards the end of the third year, lasts until the height of the bush is approximately 2 m. It consists of:
a) **capping**: cutting off the **terminal bud** of the stem, sometimes carried out in several successive stages at 0.6 m, 1.2 m and 1.8 m to enable a solid frame to be created. (Capped multiple-stem at 1.8 m is also practised in East Africa.) The branches rise in tiers on several levels, only one of the developed suckers being retained at each capping. In order to prevent the top of the stem from fanning out, due to the weight of the horizontal branches, one of the two primary terminal branches should be removed;
b) **removal** of excessively low **primaries** (primary branches) which reach the ground or are less than 30 cm above the ground;
c) **removal** of **primary branches** which are closer together than 15 cm, beginning with the weakest; this should be carried out carefully, since these branches are not renewable;
d) **removal** of **secondary branches** arising from the two nodes nearest to the trunk and **cutting back** all the adventitious shoots on the primary branches which are not growing in the required direction, as well as suckers on the stem. The purpose of all this pruning is to open up the bush so that light and plant protection sprays can penetrate more easily and to reduce the risk of fruit-bearing branches breaking. Retaining only two to ten vigorous, well spread-out lateral shoots per primary branch will also allow for adequate ventilation within the plant canopy. When modified in this manner, the shrub will be approximately 2 m high, with 40 – 50 primary branches, the longest of which will have been reduced to 0.6 m by capping.

It must not be forgotten that primary branches do not have the capacity to regenerate.

Fruiting and maintenance phase
After the primaries have fruited, most of the fruits will be produced on

46

the secondary, as well as on the lateral branches.

To achieve this, routine pruning will consist of:

- cutting off any weakened or excessively long branches which have already produced fruit;
- capping the primaries, if necessary, to stimulate the growth of secondary branches which should be maintained at a length of 0.6 m;
- removing any dead or infected wood, and restricting the number of secondaries to no more than two per node;
- removal of suckers at regular intervals of about six weeks, particularly in the rainy season. This is particularly important since capping stimulates the development of axillary buds on the stem.

Rejuvenation or renewal phase

When pathogens or climatic changes damage the main stem, it may be possible to compensate for this by introducing a replacement stem in the form of a sucker arising from a node on the lower part of the main stem.

The single stem may have to be renewed at a later date, between 15 and 25 years, if the foliage begins to die back and production reaches an economically unacceptable level, although the root system may still be vigorous. Renewal of the single stem will, in this case, be effected by cutting back of the old trunk, using an oblique cut, at a distance of 30 cm from the ground.

Advantages and disadvantages of single-stem pruning

The main advantage of this method is that regular production can be permanently achieved at an optimum economic level on all the plots in the plantation.

Single-stem pruning permits the use of automatic harvesters which are currently in use in some production areas. The main advantage of this system is that production on secondary branches makes it appropriate for use with many commonly grown species and varieties which naturally produce fruits on secondary growths. These include *C. Arabica* var. *typica*, Mundo Novo hybrids and certain clones of *C. Canephora*.

The main disadvantage of this method lies in its cost, due to the many cultural operations which are necessary. These require careful planning and a skilled workforce. The main pruning, the so-called **formative pruning**, is estimated to be the most labour-intensive task; an average worker being able to prune between 50 and 60 trees a day.

Multiple-stem pruning

The multiple-stem system of pruning is used on coffee plants from which the fruit is to be harvested mainly from the primary branches. There is therefore a need to replace them periodically with new fruiting stems. The technique which is recommended for rejuvenating the plants in five

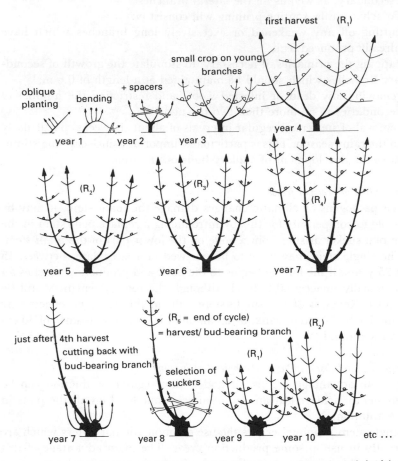

first harvest (R₁)

small crop on young branches

oblique planting

bending

+ spacers

year 1   year 2   year 3   year 4

(R₂)   year 5

(R₃)   year 6

(R₄)   year 7

just after 4th harvest cutting back with bud-bearing branch

(R₅ = end of cycle) = harvest/ bud-bearing branch

selection of suckers

(R₁)

(R₂)

year 7   year 8   year 9   year 10   etc ...

Fig 31   *Five-yearly multiple-stem pruning with bud-bearing branch on robusta hybrid (grown from seedling)*

year cycles is called 'five-yearly, multiple-stem pruning with bud-bearing branch' (Fig 31).

Formative phase

The formation of the multiple stems which may vary from three to five, depending on the richness of the soil and the spacing of the plants, may be carried out by the following methods:

• Removing suckers which have grown on the original stump;
• Planting the stem at an angle;
• Bending the one-year-old plant ('Agobio');
• Early double capping to form a double or quadruple pyramidal shape. This is typical of the system used in Costa Rica;

- In East Africa, for both arabica and robusta, the young seedlings are capped at the nursery or in the first three to four months after field planting, to raise two stems in the first cycle, followed by two to three stems in subsequent cycles depending on plant population.

At the normal time of planting, vigorous plants are taken from the nursery and are planted at an angle of 30 degrees to the vertical; a triangular frame made of cardboard or plywood may be used to obtain the correct angle. Six months later, six shoots will be selected, in order to provide for any losses that may occur. Two months later, three or four vigorous shoots will be selected for retention. They should preferably originate low on the main stem. The shoots which are to be eliminated are cut back to the stump, using secateurs.

This procedure allows the shoots selected to develop relatively rapidly in full light, which will encourage the production of short internodes.

Eight to ten months after planting, an inspection will show that some plants will not have developed lateral shoots. These plants, which are already partially lignified but still pliable, are then bent over at an angle of 45 degrees by a progressive and careful series of bending procedures. The stem will be kept in a bent position using either a tie and a stake or a wooden hook approximately 0.5 m long. The tips of the branches pointing towards the ground should be removed. Two to three months later, several suckers will have developed as a result of the bending process.

Fruiting and maintenance phase
No specialised pruning of the green wood takes place during the early growing period and the first five years of production. The stems grow freely up to a height at which they are suitable for harvesting without the use of ladders.

The only usual maintenance required is the successive removal of suckers at intervals of six weeks to two months during the rainy season when growth is rapid, using secateurs. Care must be taken to avoid injuring the cushion of dormant buds, which will subsequently be used in the renewal of the old stems. All dead or diseased wood should also be removed.

Rejuvenation or renewal phase
This is carried out by periodically cutting back the high, declining and marginally productive stems. The stems are first cut back after seven years of growth for clones from early fruiting cultivars; at eight years for plants of later fruiting hybrids or after five harvests. The process will then be repeated every five years.

The use of spacers in the early formative years of the goblet-shaped bush with multiple stems may prolong the development cycle by one year or ensure a reasonable height of bush for harvesting at the end of five years, particularly in regions where the climate and cloud cover tend to promote stem extension.

All the stems on the stump, except for one, are cut back. This stem is retained as the bud-bearing branch. From an economic point of view, this bud-bearing branch will provide a crop at the end of the year in which the plant was cut back. The stem which is selected from the three or four stems should be the one which is most likely to produce fruit. It should, if possible, originate on the side of the plant where it would least interfere with exposure of the stump to the sun, so that the young suckers which develop will receive as much light as possible. This will also promote the development of vigorous new shoots.

The plants are **stumped** or cut back to a height of 0.3 m, using a pruning saw and making an oblique cut in order to prevent rainwater collecting on the wound. Using a machete for this pruning is not recommended since it produces irregular cuts, with consequent splitting of the wood. A power-driven saw may speed up the main operation but requires the assistance of another worker to hold the stems in order to avoid stripping the bark from the stump.

It is recommended that the wounds are painted over to prevent attack by fungi or pests. Coal tar, horticultural mastic or old engine oil to which 10 per cent dieldrin has been added are possible materials.

The timing of the operation should be during the dry season and as soon as possible after harvesting, to promote early growth of the new shoots which should flower one year later. Otherwise one harvest will be lost during the cycle, making this form of pruning uneconomical.

The plot, which will be subject to more light penetration as a result of the removal of three quarters of the canopy, is likely to be rapidly invaded by weeds, in particular, grasses. Considerable attention should, therefore, be paid to routine cultivations, such as regular row weeding, and cultivating the soil between the rows up to 1 m from the foot of the trees, using a hoe or rotovator. Plastic covers will be necessary, particularly where chemical weeding is practised, to prevent any of the chemical from drifting onto the young stems.

Three months after cutting back, the first selective thinning out of the developing suckers is carried out, at which stage the suckers will be 0.25 – 0.30 m in length. Three to six of the most robust shoots are retained. These should be evenly distributed around the stump.

One to two months later, the suckers should be thinned out again, removing any new shoots and finally retaining three or four vigorous stems.

One year later, after harvesting, the bud-bearing branch should be removed, using the pruning method already described for stumping.

A new production cycle begins with the growth of the new stems which will form the main branches. The crop on the one-year stem will be small, but should be followed by three good to very good harvests, with the cycle ending with a small crop on the bud-bearing branch which should be roughly equivalent to that obtained on the young stems.

For robusta, in the Central African Republic, the harvests illustrated below were estimated as a percentage of average production, during three years of good harvest.

	% of average production	Tonnes/ha
Young stems	36%	0.720
2nd harvest	130%	2.600
3rd harvest	87%	1.740
4th harvest	83%	1.660
Bud-bearing branch	37%	0.740

Thus an average annual harvest of 2 tonnes per hectare at 100 per cent of average production is achieved on the adult stems; with an annual average for the full cycle of 1.492 tonnes per hectare.

A relationship exists between multiple-stem pruning and the density of planting, which influences the number of stems retained on each bush. The number of stems per hectare which is compatible with good productivity, is around 5000. The use of fertilisers and good standards of cultivation will allow for a higher number of fruiting stems to be established, with 6000 or more per hectare being possible with vigorous trees. The distance between plants in the row is also a factor to be considered in determining the number of stems which are to be retained on each stump. Thus a density of 2000 trees per hectare (the former standard for arabica) with a spacing of 2 m × 2.5 m, would support the growth of three fruiting stems per tree, while, for robusta, a density of less than 1330 trees per hectare with a spacing of 3 m × 2.5 m would require at least four stems per stump.

Advantages and disadvantages of multiple-stem pruning
The main advantage of this method lies in the simplicity of its implementation; no skilled labour is required and the operations can be carried out fairly rapidly. It is, moreover, well suited to the growth response of canephora and many of its hybrids.

The drawbacks arise mainly from the duration of the cycle and from the variations imposed on production during the cycle. During a five-year cycle, for example, three good harvests alternate with two small harvests, obtained from the young stems and bud-bearing branch. It may also happen that the third good crop, in the fourth year of the cycle, may develop mainly on fairly high branches, and it may not be fully picked. This emphasises the advantage of having early spacers which will retard growth to some extent.

The bushy habit of the stump branches and their height make them unsuitable for mechanical picking by the automatic harvesters which are currently available.

An excessive number of stems per tree and the interlacing of their internal secondary branches may also complicate plant protection treatment.

In spite of these drawbacks, the low cost of the method has led to it being adopted on many commercial plantations, even including those growing arabica as in East Africa. It is also possible to stabilise the level of production of the entire plantation by applying it with the same frequency as the single-stem system, that is by dividing the area into equal parts and planting successively as many plots as there are years of the pruning cycle operated, as in East Africa.

With the time lag necessarily imposed by a five-year system, the years of high productivity on three fifths of the plants compensate, at least in theory, for the low productivity of the two fifths of the crop produced on the bud-bearing branches and young stems, subject to the variability of climatic conditions. A good average production therefore becomes established, enabling full use to be made of all the human and material resources which are employed in the production of these crops.

Natural free growth, with accelerated periodical renewal
This is a non-pruning system in which the planter essentially allows the bushes to develop naturally. There is therefore no formative pruning or pruning to improve fruiting, unless it is spasmodic maintenance, involving the occasional removal of suckers and removal of dead and diseased wood. Since the plant is not capped, there is considerable self-shading within the canopy.

This method is used mainly on dwarf varieties, which are densely planted. It does, however, involve a renewal process, that is cutting back some of the main stems at fairly frequent intervals, normally every three harvests, in order to avoid a serious drop in production.

Conclusion

It should be remembered that pruning is not, in itself, a panacea, in that it does not modify the performance of the bushes as intensively as do the normal plantation maintenance techniques such as weeding, mulching and plant protection measures. It does, however, enable productivity to be maintained by controlling growth and fruiting, and is therefore a very important factor in determining the profitability of a plantation.

Nevertheless, the vital importance of periodically removing the suckers should be recognised since the effect on the resulting crop at the end of the season is roughly comparable to that of weeding. Thorough weeding and sucker removal may sometimes result in an increase in the crop of around 100 kg of commercial coffee per hectare.

Any system must be adapted to the biological characteristics of the type of coffee being grown, such as dwarf or tall varieties, hard, soft, flexible or brittle stems or branches, or their susceptibility to damage by the weather. The growing environment including the plantation layout and density of planting, level of shading, mechanisation of maintenance operations and harvesting, and the human involvement such as the availability, cost and professional skill of the labour force, as well as the economic conditions of the plantation, are all factors which should be considered when assessing the viability of the production system.

Any regular pruning system, which is to result in increased productivity, depends on the soil having sufficient nutritional resources, otherwise it is essential that this is remedied artificially by applying mineral and/or organic fertilisers.

Once a given method of pruning has been adopted, it should be implemented with the appropriate amount of skill and continuity, otherwise the shrubs will degenerate into thick bushes with a low production potential.

3.3 Fertilisers

The use of mineral and organic fertilisers is an important technique which can improve the productivity of coffee plants, provided that the investment is made viable by a wise choice of fertiliser, and that this is applied on plantations which are well run and well maintained.

The purpose of applying fertiliser is, however, two-fold; namely, to meet the nutritional needs of the coffee plant and to preserve the mineral and organic balance of the soil in order to maintain its structure and fertility. This involves the pH level of the soil solution, the potassium/calcium ratio, linked with the magnesium status, the nitrogen/phosphorous and the carbohydrate/nitrogen ratios.

Fertiliser trials often have to be carried out to determine the nature and the rate of application of the fertilisers to be used, in order to adjust them to the characteristics and conditions of a given piece of land. The nutritional requirements of the plant are most effectively studied by analysing the plant tissues at different stages of growth, including the harvested crop. Leaf diagnosis, in particular, is a method which is most likely to provide information on the levels of optimum nutrition and on the fluctuations which occur in the chemical composition of the plant at any given moment during the annual cycle. This is valuable information when a timetable for applying the fertiliser has to be prepared.

> *Careful maintenance of the soil and of the coffee bushes is essential if the use of fertilisers is to have maximum effect on the crop.*

Below and above these optimum levels, deficiencies or excesses of an element may occur and will be apparent in the leaves of the coffee plant which will exhibit various symptoms (Figs 32 and 33).

Soil analysis of many coffee plantations has, however, enabled statistical data on their chemical reserves to be compiled, and it has been possible to relate the level of growth and productivity of the coffee plants to the chemical reserves existing in the soils in which they are planted.

> *In general, nitrogen, which is particularly necessary for the young coffee plant, can also have a favourable effect on the level of the harvest obtained.*

On the basis of various studies, it can be stated that:

- The nitrogen and phosphorus requirements of young coffee plants are particularly high, whereas the requirements of mature, fruiting plants are mainly for nitrogen and potassium; these are often linked with the available magnesium;
- On partially unsaturated soils, which are often adequately supplied with potassium, coffee plants only respond to nitrogen, or, after a certain number of years of production, to nitrogen and phosphorus;
- On unsaturated soils, with a poor exchange capacity, if the levels of exchangeable bases, in particular potassium, are low, the coffee plants will need a complete NPK fertiliser with added magnesium.

The information held by coffee research centres therefore enables advice to be given concerning types of fertiliser, their application rates and optimum periods of application.

On young plantations, in order to avoid temporary toxicity problems, no fertiliser should be applied during the three months following transplanting. Any applications should then be divided and applied at intervals of about three months.

Four applications per year would normally be adequate to ensure continuous growth during the rainy season and to reduce nutrient losses through leaching. However, planters are generally limited by the availability of labour; one working day being required to spread two to three 50 kg bags. Two applications each year are generally adequate for adult

Fig 32   *Potassium deficiency (LOUÉ collection)*

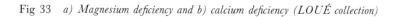

Fig 33   *a) Magnesium deficiency and b) calcium deficiency (LOUÉ collection)*

Upper surface: Lower surface:
'oily' transparency of the infested zones   powdery orange areas

Fig 34   *Attack by orange rust (*Hemileia vastatrix*) on a* C. arabica *leaf (Sergio GIL collection)*

coffee plants and this would normally be an acceptable compromise between biological necessity and effective use of labour.

> *The use of balanced, complete (NPK) fertilisers is necessary when soil fertility is considered to be low.*

Practical application methods for mineral fertilisers

Composition of the fertilisers

Nitrogen: a very important element which is widely applied, particularly in the form of ammonium sulphate which contains 21 per cent nitrogen. This has a longer lasting effect than compounds which contain nitrates; it also supplies sulphur (23 per cent) which is useful both to the plant and to the micro-organisms in the soil. The ammonia is efficiently absorbed by the colloidal complex in the soil which gradually returns it to the soil solution. It is an acidifying fertiliser, which is an advantage on fairly neutral soils with a pH of 7, but should not be applied to coffee plants growing in soils which are already very acidic, e.g. having a pH of less than 4.

Urea: is non-toxic to plants, and is the nitrogenous fertiliser containing the most nitrogen (40 – 45 per cent). It is, relatively, the least expensive fertiliser to use.

Some agricultural experts also suggest the use of CAN (calcium ammonium nitrate) on coffee plants, since it supplies nitrogen at 20 – 34.5 per cent, depending on the calcium content, in the two most soluble assimilable forms. This is ideal in acidic soils while ASN (ammonium sulphate nitrate) is also used in fairly neutral soils. Both are widely used in East Africa.

Phosphorus: promotes the mobilisation of nitrogen and potassium in the soil. Excessive applications should never be carried out since this could result in the soil rapidly becoming exhausted of these two elements. In acid soils, the use of natural phosphates (35 per cent P_2O_5), or better still of dicalcium phosphates (35 – 42 per cent of P_2O_5) is recommended. In soils which are almost neutral or are slightly alkaline, it would be preferable to use superphosphates (single, 14 – 20 per cent, double 40 per cent or triple 50 per cent P_2O_5).

Potassium: promotes and supplements the use of nitrogen in the soil by creating complex compounds in the vegetative tissues and the beans of the coffee plant. It plays a role in the formation of the sugars and reserve materials in the seed and increases the plant's resistance to drought.

The element may be supplied in the form of a sulphate (48 per cent K_2O) or as a chloride, (63 per cent K_2O), which is relatively soluble. At least two applications should be made per annum, but the chlorine content may sometimes be toxic to certain coffee plants. Potassium nitrate (44 per cent K and 13 per cent N), which is very soluble, has the advantage of supplying in one compound, two of the essential nutritive elements.

Magnesium: is most commonly supplied in the form of dolomite, a double carbonate of lime and magnesium (40 per cent – 45 per cent CaO plus 30 – 35 per cent MgO). Magnesium is an important element in chlorophyll production.

Complete fertilisers

The formulae of complete fertilisers, which are detailed on the bags, indicate the respective percentages of the useful elements which is equivalent to the number of fertilising units per 100 kg of fertiliser contained in the bag. These units are given in the order N, P, K and Mg, if present, followed by the trace elements contained in the mixture. The most commonly used fertilisers in coffee-growing are 10–5–20, 10–10–20, 12–10–15, 12–8–18 and, most popular of all, 20–10–10. Their application is often accompanied by an additional dressing of a simple nitrogenous fertiliser.

Trace elements

The physiological activity and catalytic role of various micro-elements are important in the mineral nutrition of the coffee plant. These include iron, manganese, boron, zinc and copper.

Although they are required by the plant in very low concentrations, hence their name, deficiencies in one or other of these elements are often reported and become apparent in the leaves of the bushes. They frequently occur in plants grown in volcanic or sandy soils. They may sometimes be the result of a deficiency in the metabolism of the bush.

Such deficiencies are often corrected by the controlled spraying of solutions of zinc sulphate, borax or organo-metallic chelates on the leaves.

Fertiliser application methods

Surface applications of nitrogenous fertilisers are recommended. These nitrify rapidly, are very soluble and easily reach a soil depth of 10 – 30 cm. On the other hand, a light hoeing or forking in will improve the action of phosphate and potassium-based fertilisers, as well as that of complete fertilisers.

The ideal method of applying the fertiliser to the soil, particularly in the case of young plants, is in a ring around the edge of the leaf canopy from where the rain normally drips to the ground (Fig 35).

In the mature coffee plantation, spreading the fertiliser broadcast along the rows, by hand or mechanically, may encourage root extension between the rows.

As already stated, it is also possible to spray the leaves, particularly

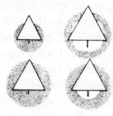 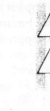 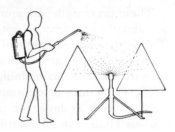

| in circles – in rings | in linear bands | leaf spraying, manually or |
| (directly below the foliage) | (at the edge of the foliage) | by sprinkling |

Fig 35   *Methods of spreading fertilisers*

with urea and phosphates. The application of minerals can also be achieved by dissolving them in an irrigation system, or even mixing them with plant protection sprays (Fig 35).

As far as the timing is concerned, although the phosphates can be applied in a single dressing, usually at the beginning of the rainy season, nitrogen and potassium should be applied in three or four dressings. It has been observed, for example, that an excessive amount of potassium may create a deficiency of calcium and magnesium. Furthermore, on sandy soils with low retentive properties, there is a risk that the soluble potassium will not be fixed in the soil and will be rapidly leached.

Organic manures and soil fertility

The application of organic material often adds to the effectiveness of applications of mineral fertilisers by improving the 'clay-humus' complex of the soil. This acts as a buffer between the soil and the plant by first retaining, and then progressively releasing, the elements which are applied.

It is difficult to alter the clay content of a soil. However, it is possible to prevent the soil from becoming degraded. This may occur due to erosion by rain which carries the finer particles deep into the soil, leaving only coarser elements and sand on the surface. In humid, tropical climates, the formation of metallic concretions on the surface may occur due to laterisation, which changes the silica/alumina and iron ratio due to the silica being leached out.

These problems can be reduced by conserving the soil in various ways, such as avoiding burning residues and dried vegetation on the land during clearing and by not ploughing too deeply or disturbing the ground excessively between the planted rows. Contour planting should be used in areas which are at risk from erosion.

59

These preventative measures should be supplemented by steps which are aimed to preserve, if not to increase, the humus content of the soil. This is the main objective of mulching, and approximately 25 tonnes of mulch per hectare are required at a depth of 10 cm. Interplanting a green manure crop or maintaining a cover crop and spreading natural or artificial manures or compost made from the by-products of coffee-processing, such as husks or parchment, and using vegetable wastes of various kinds, can all contribute to the fertility of the soil and prevent erosion (Fig 36).

Fig 36   *Mulching or growing a cover crop between the rows*

These later measures are often the only method practised by a smallholder or in home gardens where the coffee plots are close to villages.

The recommended rates of application of organic manures are 15 – 25 kg/year for four trees and the most popular methods of application are either spreading, following by a light hoeing or forking, or burying, either in an open trench between the rows or in a circular or semi-circular trench around the bushes. Care should be taken not to injure the surface roots of the coffee plants during these operations.

It should be borne in mind that a dressing of an organic material requires an additional 'top-up' of a nitrogenous or nitrophosphate-based fertiliser, that is 6 – 8 kg of nitrogen per tonne of mulch or equivalent, otherwise the coffee plants may show signs of yellowing due to nitrogen starvation caused by an intensification of microbial development in the soil.

Fig 37   *Adult 'Java' coffee plants. Cameroon (BOUHARMONT collection)*

Experiments with fertilisers carried out on both arabica and robusta species have proved that the use of mineral fertilisers can increase production by between 30 per cent and 70 per cent and even by 100 per cent, when combined with mulching. However, this improvement in productivity due to the use of fertilisers is only profitable on a plantation yielding at least 500 to 700 kg per hectare of marketable coffee before fertiliser application.

4 Soil conservation and particular problems in coffee growing

4.1 *Conservation of the soil and anti-erosion measures*

The natural ecological balance of the inter-tropical zones which are suitable for growing coffee is provided by forest. This may be dense, equatorial forest, more lightly wooded forest or savanna with trees in the drier tropics or at high altitudes.

Any alteration in the ecological complex of the forest due to cultivation, leads to a fairly rapid breakdown of the fertility of the surface soil. This occurs as a result of the combined interaction of the climatic factors such as rain, wind, sunshine, or biological factors such as microbial activity in the soil and human interference.

The name given to this breakdown is **erosion**, which may be due to water or wind, depending on its nature. Erosion by rainfall is the most obvious and may be the most serious form of erosion as far as the humid, coffee-growing regions are concerned.

The coffee plantation is particularly sensitive to this form of erosion when the ground is being prepared for planting and also when the young plants are becoming established. The severity of erosion will depend on the topography, the nature and the frequency of rainfall, the planting layout and the growing methods being used. Clean weeding in particular should be avoided.

Methods of erosion control

When the various factors causing erosion have been identified by observation and experimentation, the following solutions may be introduced:

Adoption of a suitable planting layout
The best solution would be to adopt a form of **contour planting**. The technique used would depend on the gradient of the slope and might involve growing alternate strips of coffee plants and cereals, ground cover plants or vegetables. Alternatively, coffee plants could be grown in hedges

or in anti-erosion strips in association with cover crops such as *Flemingia*, *Tephrosia* or *Crotalaria*.

Minimum maintenance growing methods

Above all, it is essential not to plough too deeply nor to intensively cultivate the soil between the rows. This would stimulate the activity of soil micro-organisms, resulting in an accelerated rate of destruction of the humus, leading to undesirable change in soil structure and fertility.

Farmers are therefore advised to work the soil as little as possible, particularly in the rainy season. Consequently, the methods which involve minimal cultivation are recommended. In order of preference these would be: mulching, which is ideal but costly to implement; chemical weeding, which requires skill on the part of those involved and the availability of good herbicides; the establishment of living and permanent ground cover; artificial mulching by using black plastic film, mainly used on young plantations – this is effective but costly. It is often preferable to use a rotary crusher rather than a rotovator, unless it can be adjusted to provide a very superficial raking effect. Finally, scything or cutting back weeds or cover crops with a machete or cutlass is always less damaging than weeding, but the effect is short-lived and it is therefore a costly process in terms of labour. It also has the disadvantage of propagating certain stoloniferous or rhizomatous species, which regenerate from cut pieces of stem or root. Re-seeding by rapidly growing species may also occur.

The best system to adopt, therefore, depends mainly on the technical and economic resources of the farmer.

Planting permanent ground cover crops

This method is one which protects the soil at the least cost. Allowance should be made, however, for the cost of the seeds or cuttings, the planting operation and various unavoidable maintenance costs. It is also essential that the species used as a ground cover crop is suitable (Fig 38).

This produces a living soil cover, resistant to inclement weather conditions, with the exception of frost in arabica-growing regions which are prone to this hazard. It is, therefore, quite different from the clean weeding system and is strongly recommended for use in all regions where there is high rainfall and frequent storms. The technique involves growing the cover crop in bands between the rows of coffee plants, leaving only the row of bushes to be weeded, either in strips or rings around each plant.

After experimenting with many species, the IRCC (Research Institute for Coffee, Cocoa and other Stimulant Plants) recommends the following leguminous plants for use in the humid tropics. They are also useful for

63

Fig 38   *Plantation of* C. arabica *coffee plants with* Flemingia *sp. ground cover. Cameroon (BOUHARMONT collection)*

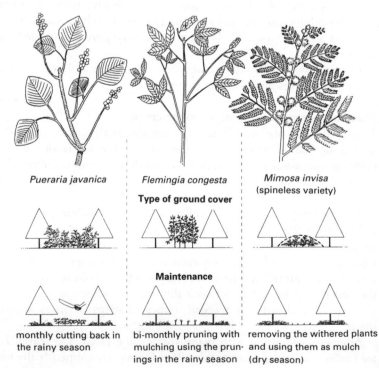

Pueraria javanica	Flemingia congesta	Mimosa invisa (spineless variety)
	Type of ground cover	
	Maintenance	
monthly cutting back in the rainy season	bi-monthly pruning with mulching using the prunings in the rainy season	removing the withered plants and using them as mulch (dry season)

Fig 39   *Ground cover plants*

the additional nitrogen enrichment they give to the soil due to the activity of the nitrogen-fixing bacteria in their root nodules (Fig 39).

Mimosa invisa: has a non-twining, prostrate habit. The spineless variety is normally sown at a rate of four to five kilograms of selected seed per hectare, exceptionally up to ten kilograms. This species is easy to plant; the seed is sown broadcast and the plants rapidly suppress weeds if it is sown densely. It does, however, pose a fire risk, since the plants wither in the dry season.

Maintenance consists simply of raking over the dry remains of the plants at the end of the growing season covering the soil around the base of the coffee plants, if there is no risk of fire. Selective weeding-out of any plants of the spiny mimosa which develop is essential. The spineless mimosa regenerates rapidly from seed when the rains begin again. Its use is recommended in very damp areas where the wild spiny variety does not normally occur.

Other non-twining, prostrate-growing species which can be used are *Desmodium ovalifolium* (green leaf), *Desmodium intortum* (silver leaf) and *Centrosema pubescens*.

Pueraria javanica: has a twining habit. It multiplies easily from seed which is sown at the same volume per hectare as recommended for *Mimosa*, or from cuttings. It produces abundant perennial foliage during the dry season and provides a good ground cover, very effectively choking weeds. Its twining stems, however, covering the coffee bushes, could kill them if they are not cut back regularly using a machete or a cutlass at least once a month in the rainy season. *Pueraria* is difficult to re-establish after it has died out. Maintenance consists mainly of raking the stems towards the middle line of the inter-row to clear the soil on either side of the coffee plants.

Calopogonium mucunoides, also twining, may be treated in a similar way to *Pueraria*.

Flemingia congesta: has a non-twining, erect habit, providing good ground cover. It is propagated by seeds sown between the coffee rows in drills (three to four, at intervals of 0.4 m), or in clusters of five to eight seeds, in individual seed holes 30 – 40 cm apart, at a seed rate of 10 – 20 kg/ha. It requires a soil with a fairly high organic content for good germination. The young seedlings will require several selective weedings. Since it competes actively with the root system of the coffee plant during its early stages of development, it should preferably be established before the coffee is planted. However, as a mature plant, it has a deep, non-competitive root system, absorbing mineral elements from the lower levels of the soil and transporting them to its leaves. These nutrients are returned to the soil surface as litter at leaf fall or when the stems are cut back. A bi-monthly cutting back, during the rainy season, is normally a routine cultivation and provides a quantity of organic mulch which inhibits weed growth. Plants regenerate rapidly after cutting back, which is generally carried out before they produce seeds. It is possible, and even advisable, however, to leave a few rows untouched, keeping them as windbreaks and for seed production. *Flemingia* is an excellent ground cover plant, providing mulch and shelter from strong wind but, apart from the problems associated with its germination, it is also vulnerable to various types of root rot and attack by insects which also feed on the coffee plant.

Other erect, leguminous plants which can be used, alone or in combination with *Flemingia* are *Crotalaria striata* or *C. juncea*, *Tephrosia* spp. or *Cassia alata*.

Tithonia diversifolia: a member of the family Compositae, provides a large mass of mulch, but has to be controlled very closely, otherwise it tends to be invasive and competes fiercely with the coffee plants.

Mixed farming

This combination of coffee cultivation and animal rearing provides a supply of manure which makes a valuable contribution to the humus content of the soil of the coffee plantation. Some ground cover plants, such as *Pueraria* and *Centrosema*, are also useful fodder crops. In Africa, it should be stressed that, if cattle are to be included in the system, there is the risk of the tsetse fly spreading sleeping sickness. Sheep can also provide manure and assist in weed control, but sheep or cattle among the coffee plants could also damage branches by trampling or grazing.

Shading

The advantages already mentioned which shade trees provide in coffee plantations are mechanical protection against erosion caused by rain/hail provided by their foliage and roots; protection of the soil and plants against excessive fluctuations in air temperature and the supply of leaf litter which enriches the humus content of the soil. The disadvantages arising from the use of shade trees together with their usefulness in marginal coffee-growing areas have also been discussed (page 13).

Interception or drainage terraces

This is a last resort measure because of the size of the investment which has to be made to install these and maintain them. The absorption terraces which will reduce the erosive effects of the rain, and upon which the coffee plants will be planted, can be built in embankments (steps). They may be individual terraces i.e. one per coffee plant, or large scale, the latter requiring the use of large earth-moving machinery after a topographical survey has been carried out (Fig 40).

The trenches and protective ridges consist of:
- **Blind trenches**: these are excavated between the rows of coffee plants;
- **Box-terraces**: these are circular ridges built around each plant. They

Fig 40   *Kajoernas, Indonesia. Background: arabica with rubber (*Hevea*). Foreground: young arabica plantation illustrating contour planting*

also serve as an irrigation basin in the dry season, but are not recommended for use in regions liable to frost, since they may act as a collecting area or buffer for the cold air.

4.2   Problems specific to coffee growing

Shading

Permanent shading moderates the physiological growth cycles of coffee bushes which are caused by full light and climatic variations, but it is really only useful in locations which are marginal due to altitude or latitude. In Latin America, for example, shading is recommended in those coffee plantations which are situated in high altitude regions and are therefore at risk, mainly in order to preserve the soil from erosion by rain.

Leguminous types of shade tree such as *Albizzia, Erythrina, Gliricidia, Inga* and *Leucaena* are normally planted at low densities i.e. 12 × 12 m to 18 × 18 m (Figs 41 and 42).

The disadvantages associated with the use of shade, when it is used excessively and is not regulated, are depressed yield, increase in production costs, risk of the development of disease in humid conditions, competition for water and food and damage to the coffee plants caused by fallen branches damaged in high winds. These often offset the advantages.

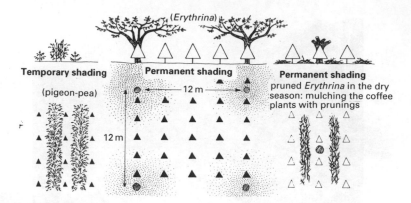

Temporary shading

(pigeon-pea)

Permanent shading

← 12 m →

12 m

Permanent shading

pruned *Erythrina* in the dry season: mulching the coffee plants with prunings

(Erythrina)

Fig 41 *Shading*

Fig 42 *Plantation of arabica under shade. Cameroon (HOCHDOERFFER collection)*

It is therefore not advisable to use permanent shade unless the ecological conditions are borderline for the cultivation of coffee, i.e. areas exposed to frost, hail and excesses of temperature or rain, or when the growing methods do not take full advantage of the means of production, such as in family-run plantations with variable financial incomes.

Temporary shading of young coffee plantations for a period of one to two years, by planting more slender bushes between the rows such as *Cajanus cajan* (pigeon pea), *Tephrosia* spp., *Crotalaria* spp. and *Flemingia congesta*, does, however, offer more advantages than disadvantages.

Windbreaks

While the use of shade trees is sometimes controversial, the use of wind-breaks, on the other hand, is generally considered to be of vital import-ance in coffee-growing.

The presence of windbreaks planted approximately perpendicular to the prevailing wind is useful not only in regions where violent, destructive winds blow in certain seasons, but also in zones exposed to moderate, regular winds such as sea and land breezes, trade winds, the harmattan in West Africa, convective winds in mountainous regions, etc. In such areas, these winds, which create light but regular turbulence, increase both evaporation from the leaves and the plant's water requirement. This may periodically cause stress due to water loss which is detrimental to productivity.

Two points are relevant when deciding whether or not to install wind-breaks (Fig 33):

- The **height** of the adult plants which are to form the windbreak hedge. This hedge protects a strip on the leeward side which is equal to five to seven times its height. With large trees, a windbreak hedge every 70 to 100 metres apart will therefore be sufficient. This can be reduced to between 25 and 30 metres with species which do not grow to any great height, such as unpruned *Flemingia*;
- The **thickness** and **density** of the hedge. An excessively bushy hedge creates a great deal of turbulence downstream of the air current. This is harmful to the coffee plant. It would, therefore, be preferable to have broader hedges consisting of thinly planted rows of different species at different heights, rather than a continuous and very densely planted row of one type of plant alone (Fig 43).

Species of bush most commonly used as windbreaks are *Grevillea robusta*, *Casuarina* spp. (filao), *Erythrine* spp., *Populus* spp. (poplar), *Pinus patula*, *Cypress* spp., *Eucalyptus* spp., *Flemingia congesta*, *Leucaena glauca* and bamboo species. These should all be planted at a distance of more than ten metres from the rows of coffee plants. Banana trees planted at the edge of the coffee plantation plots, have the double advantage of providing a wind-break as well as a food crop.

Intercropping

The cultivation of food crops between the rows of coffee plants is a traditional practice among small-scale farmers who are anxious to make the smallest plot of land profitable after clearing, and a vital necessity for some (Fig 44). This may, in fact, reduce the rate of growth of the bushes, particularly when the food crops are actually planted among the

69

plants as opposed to between the rows, since it may result in excessive competition, leading to yield depression of plants if maintained over too long a period in the life of the plantation.

On the other hand, experiments have shown that an interplanted crop in a strip, which is grown sufficiently distant from the base of the coffee plants (approximately 0.7 m), and which consists of selected plants which do not inhibit the growth of the young plants, far from competing with the main perennial crop, can, if well tended, contribute positively to its management. This may include protection from erosion, maintenance of a high level of biological activity in the soil and soil enrichment due to the addition of harvesting residues.

The economic advantage of this practice is undeniable in that the grower can produce a food crop while the coffee plantation is not yet productive. In an equatorial climate with two rainy seasons, or when irrigation is available, it may be possible to produce two crops a year by integrating the development cycles of two compatible crops, e.g. cereal followed by leguminous crops, or vice versa.

The advantage of this in agricultural terms is also clear. The regular application of fertiliser, weeding and plant protection treatments applied to the interplanted crop also help to maintain the productivity of the coffee plants.

The best food plants for this type of cropping are:

- Haricot beans, peanuts, *Voandzeia* (Bambarra groundnut), field peas and, in general, non-climbing leguminous plants which will enrich the soil due to the activity of their nitrogen-fixing nodules. The soil may sometimes require inoculation with the appropriate strain of nitrifying bacteria;
- Rice or maize. Maize should not be replanted continuously and should be harvested before the effect of its shade on the young coffee plants encourages weak and spindly growth, despite the favourable effect it may have as a windbreak;
- Yams, preferably grown on the flat, can occupy the inter-row alone throughout a full growing season (Fig 45).

It may also be possible to include various vegetables such as cabbages and potatoes if the climate allows, and some spice plants such as pimentos.

In contrast to the advantages referred to above, mention should be made of the constraints which are placed on the grower by some crops. These may make them unattractive or even impracticable for growing on large plantations which only produce coffee. Examples are additional expenditure, soil cultivations, maintenance, harvesting, etc.

For this reason, small multi-crop farms are those which can benefit most from these intercrops.

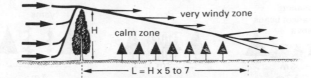

Distance protected from the wind according to the height of the windbreaks

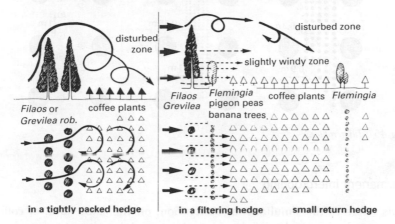

Fig 43   *Effect of windbreaks in coffee plantations*

Fig 44   *Coffee plantation. Ivory Coast*

71

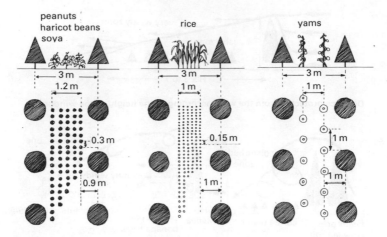

Fig 45 *Intercropping*

Permanent intercropping

This refers to the simultaneous cultivation, on the same land, of coffee plants and one or other of the tropical, perennial cash or export crops: rubber, cinchona, oil palm or coconut (Figs 46 and 47).

With the exception of this last crop, which is widely spaced and which, at the end of its growth cycle, gives relatively light shade due to its height, these intercrops are always detrimental to the optimum yields of each of the combined crops. Schweitzer, in Indonesia, calculated that there was a 30 per cent reduction in rubber and 68 per cent in coffee when the two were combined. Apart from the competition for the nutrients and water in the soil, particularly when they are planted relatively densely, there is also competition for light. This is always detrimental to the productivity of the crops if it is compared with the yield of plots under single-crop cultivation.

This combined system is therefore not recommended, even if it is carried out using plants which can be combined for a shorter period, for example banana trees.

Regeneration of old coffee plantations

Regeneration applies to those coffee plantations which have exceeded their economic life, i.e. those which have passed their normal age limit of 25 – 30 years. Beyond this, it is particularly difficult to restore declining yields due to the physiological sensitivity of most of the bushes in the plantation (Fig 48). It also applies to relatively young plantations of

Fig 46 *Padder gunnug, Kendeng lembu, Indonesia. The valley is reserved for rubber* (Hevea*) (CAMBRONY collection)*

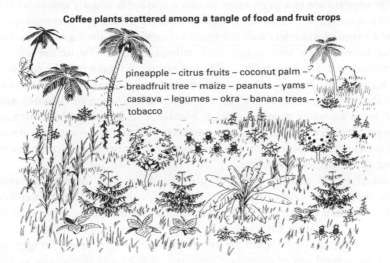

Coffee plants scattered among a tangle of food and fruit crops

pineapple – citrus fruits – coconut palm –
breadfruit tree – maize – peanuts – yams –
cassava – legumes – okra – banana trees –
tobacco

Fig 47 *The 'Antillian' garden*

15 – 20 years maximum, which show declining yields.

This onset of premature ageing generally arises during prolonged periods of low coffee prices accompanied by a reduction of production costs, at the end of a lease, or, most frequently, when there is a change of owner.

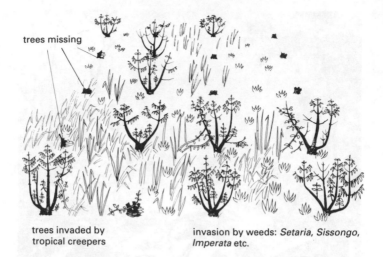

trees missing

trees invaded by
tropical creepers

invasion by weeds: *Setaria, Sissongo, Imperata* etc.

Fig 48   *Old, neglected coffee plantation*

The appearance of a plantation in this situation is usually one in which a large number of bushes are missing; those which have survived may show a range of disorders and the effects of neglect on their growth habit. These may include incomplete and unbalanced stem structure and a proportion of dead or partially defoliated branches which may be invaded by creepers. The root system may have produced a small number of roots with the root hairs and lateral roots damaged by insects or diseases and decayed to a greater or lesser extent. Finally, a number of weeds such as *Imperata, Paspalum* and *Eupatorium*, may have invaded the inter-row areas.

It is clear that regeneration requires very different remedial treatments, suited to the degree of decline.

Excessive age and too great a number of missing bushes or trees (more than 50 per cent of the initial number), coupled with considerable structural damage to the remainder, would make it more advisable to replant the plantation rather than attempt to rejuvenate it. In this case, the remaining stumps would be removed, one or two cross-ploughings would be carried out to eliminate as many of the roots remaining in the soil as possible; it would also be preferable to have a short cultivated or fallow period before replanting, using a leguminous plant as a cover plant.

Decline in vigour of a coffee plantation which is still young in economic and physiological terms, on the other hand, requires a more moderate treatment consisting of replanting, replacing missing plants and also those which are either dead or diseased, accompanied by a resumption

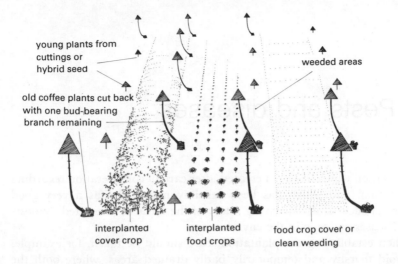

young plants from cuttings or hybrid seed

old coffee plants cut back with one bud-bearing branch remaining

weeded areas

interplanted cover crop

interplanted food crops

food crop cover or clean weeding

Fig 49 *Old coffee plantation, regenerated*

of a reasonable level of maintenance. This will produce a significant change, both in the general appearance of the plants and in their yield. The following steps should be taken (Fig 49):

1) Count and mark/peg missing bushes, if necessary preparing new planting holes and disinfecting them by spraying with copper sulphate, dusting the excavated soil with insecticide or even nematicide, then transplanting a selected variety such as a clone or high yield stock, depending on the species grown.

2) At the same time, the rest of the plantation will benefit from treating the remaining plants. This should include a pruning schedule which begins with cutting back to increase the light available for adjacent young plants, the periodical removal of suckers, plant protection treatments and treatment of the soil including fertilisation, ground cover establishment and, possibly, irrigation; all of which are necessary operations for the maintenance of a high level of productivity.

3) If necessary, particularly on small family plantations, an interplanted food crop such as cereals, leguminous plants or yams, could be grown on those plots on which the shade has been reduced during the first and sometimes the second year of rejuvenation.

5 Pests and diseases

A plantation which has been created after careful consideration regarding its location, and which has been sensibly managed, has a very good chance of successfully surviving many of the hazards presented by pests and diseases endemic in the environment.

When establishing the plantation, care should be taken, for example, to avoid marshy and temporarily badly drained areas, where both the natural vegetation and the environment provide reservoirs in which various species of harmful insects such as bugs and crickets can live and multiply. In humid, forested areas, compact clay soils are often infected with various root rot diseases and many harmful micro-organisms. Nurseries which are sited in low lying areas are particularly subject to invasion by nematodes which attack the roots.

When creating the plantation, the stumps left in place during land clearance after field burning, can shelter the larvae of stem borers which attack the trunks and branches of the coffee plants. These stumps also become hosts to various fungi, in particular members of the family Polyporaceae, the hyphae of which, in turn, will gradually infect the coffee plants.

Killing the stumps by poisoning will prevent such diseases. They should then be incinerated on the spot after soaking with potassium chlorate or nitrate. This involves pouring the chemical into holes bored into the wood, filling with clay, then soaking with petrol and burning four months later. Destroying the stumps with agricultural explosive will also remove the possibility of infestation of the coffee by borers.

The creation of a 50 m wide belt around the plantation, from which the trees have been removed and/or which has been planted with food crops, will substantially limit the degree to which the plantation is invaded by insects coming either from the adjacent forest (defoliating caterpillars, adult borers) or from adjoining neglected plantations (bugs, bark beetles).

Monitoring the condition of the bushes, i.e. inspecting the health of the plants as frequently as possible, is a fundamental precaution to be taken by the planter. This will help to prevent the spread of fungal infection or of rapid multiplication of pests which could, in extreme cases, rapidly assume epidemic proportions constituting a threat to the plantation.

A carefully maintained and manured plantation certainly offers increased resistance to such hazards, but no plantation can be totally protected against airborne, virulent, pathogenic bacteria, or against the spread of winged adult pests.

Sections 5.1 and 5.2 list the main pests and diseases affecting coffee plantations.

When control measures are planned, it must be borne in mind that they should be carried out sensibly, taking into account economic and ecological considerations, the availability of equipment and products, and the choice of the most appropriate times for treatment, such as when the pest or disease is at its most vulnerable. This may be the beginning of the reproductive phase of a population of insects, for example. The optimum intensity of spraying, rate of application and frequency are important. Excessive applications may lead to a risk of toxicity to the plant or its environment; low levels of treatment introduce the possibility of the pathogen developing tolerance, such as pests becoming resistant to some chemicals. The advice given by extension agents, based on research or, in its absence, that issued by the manufacturers of pesticides, must always be closely followed.

In most countries, the use of lindane, HCH, dieldrin, endrin and orthodifolatan is now banned and the following should be used instead:

- For foliar sprays: diazinon, sumithion, fenitrothion, gusathion;
- For dusting: malathion and dursban;
- In place of orthodifolatan: use other organic products such as daconil, delan and copper based fungicides.

Damage – symptoms	Causal agent	Pest or disease characteristics	Control methods
5.1 *Hazards to plant health in nurseries and shaded areas especially involved in raising young plants*			
The leaves turn yellow and die without visible cause; upon being uprooted, the plant roots are observed to have been severed or severely damaged.	White grubs; Coleopterous larvae of the cockchafer or melolonthid beetle type. Genera: *Apogonia*, *Adoretus* (Fig 78).	Extended underground life as large, whitish larvae with a brown head, the adults of which eat flower buds, shoots and leaves.	Manually collect adults or apply diazinon or sumithion etc. to the foliage, dust the soil around the beds with malathion or dursban at a rate of 15 g/100 m².
Ditto.	Wireworms; Coleopterous larvae of the genus *Dacus*.	Elongated, cylindrical, coriaceous, yellowish or brownish larvae (underground); the adults live in the soil and make irregular bite marks in the stem at the level of the collar.	Use poisoned bait to kill the adults (10 kg cereal flour and bran + 60 g HCH or 22.5 g endosulfan), or treat the soil with malathion or dursban at a rate of 40 g active ingredient/100 m².
Ditto.	Mole cricket *Gryllotalpa africana* (Fig 54).	Cricket with burrowing fore-legs, rapidly excavates galleries searching for larvae or worms; severs the roots.	Ditto
The leaves turn yellow and fall; the roots are observed to be infested with swollen nodules.	Nematodes; genera: *Heterodera*, *Pratylenchus*, *Tylenchus*.	Microscopic worms move through the soil water, gradually invading the roots and progressively killing the plant.	Avoid marshy areas and prolonged irrigation. Disinfect the soil with nemagon (1 kg/100 m²), phenol (0.3 l/m²), formol, steam or, on a small scale, boiling water.
Plants severed at the collar.	Tobacco cricket *Brachytrupes membranaceus*.	Very large crickets living in underground galleries. At night they sever the stems of the plantlets in order to eat them.	Hand collect any crickets sheltering under shelter traps (piles of leaves). Use bait poisoned with diazinon or sumithion. Dust the soil with malathion (5 – 7 g active ingredient/100 m²).

Symptom	Pest / Disease	Description	Control
Foliage eaten, producing a lace-like effect.	Coffee leaf skeletoniser *Leucoplema dohertyi* (Fig 56).	Small greyish cricket (7 – 8 mm) which eats the underside of the leaves, leaving the veins intact.	Spray plants with endosulfan, directing the jet upwards from underneath.
Leaves joined together, rolled up at the edges.	Leaf-rolling caterpillars *Tortricidae* spp. and *Lecythocera* spp. (Fig 55).	Small grey-brown caterpillar with a black head which jumps and twists when uncovered; joins two leaves together with a silky thread, eats the leaf parenchyma leaving the veins intact.	Spray with endosulfan at a rate of 10 g active ingredient/100 m^2, where there is rapid multiplication; otherwise leave to be checked by parasitic micro-Hymenoptera or hand pick.
The surfaces of bark, leaves and buds eaten.	Snails, slugs.	Gasteropod molluscs active mainly at night or during misty and damp days. Eggs laid in egg-cases in the ground.	Spread ashes or potassium chloride on the ground. Use poison bait with metaldehyde (plus bran) and distribute on the beds at a rate of 300 g/100 m^2 or in shelter traps. Dust with commercial granules for slug and snail control.
Plants rot at the collar, withering and dying in progressively enlarging patches.	Damping-off disease due to the fungus *Rhizoctonia solani* (Fig 76).	The disease spreads rapidly in the ground in poorly maintained nurseries or when the plants are damaged or have insect or slug bites.	Uproot and burn the dead plants. Copper-based fungicidal treatment: spraying with Bordeaux mixture or 50 per cent tetracupric oxychloride (15 g/10 l water).
The leaves are covered in brown patches with yellow haloes which may enlarge, coalesce and then drop.	Brown eye disease or Cercosporiosis: *Cercospora coffeicola*.	Common fungal disease affecting leaves in all coffee-growing regions. Damage found particularly in poorly watered and inadequately shaded nurseries.	Increase shade. Adjust level of spraying. Improve fertiliser application. Spray with preventive copper-based fungicides in regions where infection is epidemic: 1 per cent Bordeaux mixture or maneb.

Damage – symptoms	Causal agent	Pest or disease characteristics	Control methods

5.2 *Hazards to plant health in the field*

Damage to the roots and stem collar

Damage – symptoms	Causal agent	Pest or disease characteristics	Control methods
The plants yellow and die without apparent cause. Incisions can sometimes be seen on the trunk and the branches; roots are eaten away.	Cicada larvae.	Adult cicadas suck the sap of young stems and branches and lay their eggs in the resulting scars; this weakens the branches and the young stems. The larvae (white grubs) live underground for a long period. They are particularly prevalent in alluvial and light sandy soils, and several larvae may be found on each plant, the roots of which they attack.	Collect or poison the adult cicadas using systemic agents. Treat the soil with malathion (30 g in the planting hole).
Plants die progressively. When laid bare, the roots are observed to be covered in nodules.	Nematodes of various genera and species.	Concentric development of colonies of nematodes carried from one infested coffee plant to another by ground water. These microscopic worms infiltrate the root tissues which they feed on and destroy.	Prevention consists of avoiding the importation of infected plants into the nursery. Use resistant or tolerant species or varieties.
Plants die progressively. When laid bare, the roots have a brown sheath of mycelium, protecting white, scale insects.	A combination of ants and scale insects.	Disease resulting from a fungal/scale insect association living at the expense of the root sap; often found in light alluvial soils (Madagascar). Ants are the vectors of the disease.	Chemical control of ants using diazinon, sumithion or paraphene; and scale insects using oleoparathion or disulfoton.

Rapid withering of the foliage which initially turns yellow at the apex. Roots and collars crack. When the tissues are laid bare, mycelial filaments are found to be attached to the roots; various forms of fruiting bodies appear later on the collar.	Root rot: *Fomes lignosus* (white mould); *Ganoderma pseudo-ferreum* (red mould); *Phellinus lamaensis* (brown mould); *Rosellinia bunodes* (black mould); *Armillaria mellea* (agaric mould); *Clitocybe tabescens* (mould with slits).	Various fungi living in the soil on dead wood suddenly develop mycelial filaments which are parasitic on the roots. They cause these to disintegrate, leading rapidly to their death. Serious economic damage may occur if the contamination annually affects more than 3 per cent of the plants on the plantation.	Prevention: Burn dead trees using sodium chlorate and diesel oil after applying 2–4–5–T to the dead wood to encourage rotting. Direct control when only a few coffee plants affected: scrape the infected roots, wash the wounds with copper sulphate. If they are numerous, uproot plants completely and burn. Spray the turned earth with a copper-based fungicide (4 per cent copper sulphate, 1 per cent Bordeaux mixture); create a phyto-sanitary barrier to extend beyond the contaminated area. Allow the land to lie fallow, grow food crops or establish a cover crop for three to four years before replanting.
Rapid withering. The leaves initially turn yellow in a spiral pattern, the yellowing then becomes generalised and the tree dies. If the bark is lifted, black marbling can be seen along the length of the wood.	Tracheomycosis: *Gibberella xylarioides*; *Fusarium xylarioides*.	The spores of the fungus enter the vessels via wounds around the collar and the developing filaments obstruct the vessels; fissures in the bark reveal pinkish white fruiting bodies. Some species or varieties are extremely vulnerable e.g canephora.	Loosen the stumps, uproot, cut up and burn. Disinfect the soil with a copper solution. Use selected resistant varieties.

Damage – symptoms	Causal agent	Pest or disease characteristics	Control methods
Rapid withering followed by swelling and cracking; canker develops on the collar.	Fusarium bark disease: *Fusarium stilboides*.	Caused by an infective process similar to the preceding one with wounds on the trunk. A disease seen quite frequently on arabica in East Africa.	Prevention during cultivation: careful transplanting, use stakes and windbreaks. Herbicide application is preferable to using metallic tools for weeding. Disinfect all pruning tools with phenol and paint pruning wounds with tar. Curative treatment: uproot, cut up and burn the plant; disinfect the planting hole.

Damage to the trunks and branches

Damage – symptoms	Causal agent	Pest or disease characteristics	Control methods
Holes are bored into the trunk, the leaves wither and the plant partly dies. Young trunks may break in strong winds.	Stem borers are longicorn beetles belonging to the order Coleoptera. Genera: *Anthores leuconotus*, *Bixadus sierricola*, *Diphrya nigricornis* (Fig 60).	Large Coleoptera with long antennae and shimmering upper surface of the elytra. The female lays its eggs in crevices on the surface of the trunk, 16 – 20 cm from the ground. The young larvae penetrate the bark, excavate a circular gallery in the sapwood, then bore towards the heartwood. From there they excavate a descending gallery (often into the taproot below the collar), and an ascending tunnel which they extend to more than 40 cm. The larvae have a long life varying from six months to three years; sawdust is frequently present at the foot of the affected bushes.	Prevention during cultivation: separate from the forest environment by a cleared and cultivated perimeter strip. Uproot and burn any seriously affected bushes; cutting back is useless when the taproot is affected. Chemical prevention: paint the trunk up to 50 cm from the soil level with a long-lasting insecticide, e.g. 0.5 per cent emulsion. (1 l of product with 15 per cent active ingredient to 29 l of water) at three monthly intervals.

Ditto. Elliptical hole (5 – 10 mm in diameter) half way up the trunk, with a short ascending gallery.	Black borer. Genus: *Apate monachus*.	Coleopterous beetles, cylindrical, up to 2 cm long, shiny dark brown with granulated elytra; bore into the trunk and the main branches. The larvae live in the dead wood.	Cutting back is possible. Paint the trunk to half-way up with diazinon. Destroy the old stumps by burning or using an agricultural explosive.
Lower sections of branches are perforated and the ends of the branches wither. Death of the young stems and suckers occurs after cutting back. Damage is often accelerated by fungal attack such as anthracnose and tracheomycosis.	Branch scolytid beetles. *Xylosandrus* (*Xyleborus*) *morstatti* (Figs 51 and 61).	Small Coleoptera: females are shiny black, the wingless males are light brown. The female perforates and lays her eggs in the pith of the branches; the whitish larvae live in the gallery created, in symbiosis with a fungus which develops on the walls of the gallery: there may be 20 to 50 individuals, of all ages and sexes per gallery. Only the females emigrate into the open air to attack other branches; a complete cycle covers 30 – 35 days with several generations per year.	Control: cut and burn the small infested branches (possible only in cases of light infestation). Where there is rapid multiplication, destroy the migrating females by spraying the branches with long-lasting and well-adhering insecticides. Use resistant or tolerant varieties or species with large branches.
Withering of the young stems and ends of branches at the top of the bush, accompanied by leaf drop.	Xylophagous caterpillars. Genera: *Xyleutes armstrongi* (Central and West Africa), *Zeuzera coffeae* (Far East).	Young reddish caterpillars 30 – 40 mm long, or red-orange caterpillars with large white marks 20 mm long (*Zeuzera*) excavating galleries in the young stems.	Prune and manually crush or burn the dried, young branches to destroy the caterpillars and the chrysalids.

Damage – symptoms	Causal agent	Pest or disease characteristics	Control methods
Irregular bite marks on the base of the trunk.	Dusty brown beetle *Gonocephalum* (*Dacus*) *simplex* (Fig 58); see **Damage in the nursery**.		
Collar eaten away all the way round. Weakening and death of the young coffee plants.	Cutworm. Noctuid caterpillars: genus: *Agrotis*.	The caterpillars are nocturnal, 4 cm long when fully developed, dark green with two lighter longitudinal lines and four black spots per segment. They burrow into the soil during the day. Adult: grey-brown moth, with a wing-span of approximately 4 cm.	Collect the caterpillars early in the morning before they have burrowed into the soil. Use poisoned bait (bran and diazinon), see **Control in the nursery**.
Appearance of a white coating, turning pink, then reddish, on the trunk and branches; the leaves turn brown and die without falling. The bark cracks; the fruits, which are sometimes attacked, rot.	Pink disease. Fungus: *Corticium salmonicolor*.	A frequently found, non-specific disease of individual coffee plants; develops in very damp, shady places or in high density plantations.	Improve air movement by pruning or possibly removing the shading. Cut and burn the affected branches. Preventive and curative anti-fungal treatment with maneb or similar fungicide.
Trunks, leaves and branches become covered in a soot-like mould and waxy deposits; berries also infested.	Fungal filaments of *Capnodium* spp.	Frequent onset of fungal infection following attack by scale insects or aphids on the young branches. Mycelium develops on the honeydew secreted by the insects. The opacity thus created on the leaves impedes photosynthesis.	Treat plants against insects which promote the development of fungi as a secondary infection e.g. scale insects, aphids and ants.

Damage to the young branches, shoots and flower buds

Damage	Pest	Biology	Control
Invasion by various types of scale insects which weaken the infested tissues. The coffee plants may lose leaves and fruits.	Brown scale (Figs 53 and 63). Genus: *Lecanium* (soft scale); *Asterolecanium* (star scale); *Ceroplastes* (waxy scale); *Pseudococcus* (mealybugs).	Relatively common insects on coffee plants; biting and sucking mouthparts; can multiply rapidly in the dry season. Depending on the species, either one of the sexes can be mobile. May or may not be attended by ants.	Dust with parathion-diazinon. Apply oleoparathion against the waxy forms. Control ants.
Young leaves become distorted or weakened. Clusters of aphids appear, particularly on the undersides of young leaves; sooty moulds often develop on the excreted honeydew.	Aphids, genus: *Toxoptera aurantii* (Fig 62).	Sucking and biting polyphagous pests; wingless females, 1.7 mm in length, brown, oval, with a swollen abdomen; winged male, 1.6 mm length; apterous larvae with similar morphology.	Ditto.
No direct damage: Transportation and protection of the scale insects and aphids.	Ants. a great number of species. Genera: *Pheidole*, *Crematogaster*.	Nests made of earth and bundles of twigs in the forks and crevices on the surface of the tree, encouraging the spread of scale insects and aphids.	Use bait poisoned with sodium arsenite and sugar. Sticky bands on the trunks are also effective.
Galleries excavated within the branches and trunks.	Ants. Genus: *Atopomyrmex* (carpenter ants).	Directly harmful to the bush due to the excavated galleries. Other harmful Brazilian species cut young shoots and young leaves.	Dust or spray the branches with malathion (0.6 – 1 per cent) or with 0.1 per cent diazinon or with parathion (powder at 1 per cent, spray at 0.5 per cent).

Damage – symptoms	Causal agent	Pest or disease characteristics	Control methods
Relatively minor damage to the coffee plants; the leaves are joined together to construct nests; pests may give coffee growers painful bites or stings during tending of the plantation or during harvesting.	Red ants: Genera: *Oecophylla* (Fig 64); *Macromischoides*.	Little damage to the plant but a great inconvenience for the growers.	Ditto.
Young branches and young fruit attacked; they then become necrotic. Proliferation of adventitious twigs (witches brooms), deformed leaves.	Antestia mottled bug (Fig 66). Genus: *Antestiopsis*.	Eggs are laid in groups of 9 – 12 on the underside of the leaves. There are five larval stages; larvae are 1 – 3 mm in length, globular, mottled black and yellow; larval stages 40 – 90 days. Adult: winged oval aphid (7 – 7.5 mm), mottled dark green to olive brown with ivory and orange markings, one of which is a cross on the scutellum. They normally bite and suck the young cherries, the contents of which they partially empty. On the branches, terminal shoots and flower buds, their bites lead to necrosis of the tissues.	Carry out density of insect population test, spray with natural or synthetic pyrethrins; check the presence and numbers of insects per bush, selecting five trees per hectare at random. The insects are collected on a tarpaulin and, if there are more than three to five insects per tree, dust or spray with 20 per cent malathion (0.7 – 0.8 kg/hectare). This will supplement the natural control of the eggs by hymenopterous predators and of the larvae and adults by various species of mantis and other predators.
Flower buds are covered with black bites and the flowers are aborted and fail. Young leaves and terminal buds are covered with brown patches.	Mirids (Capsids) of the genus *Lygus* (length = 4 – 6 mm); genus *Volumnus* (Fig 67); (length = 6 – 7 mm); genus *Lycidocoris* (length = 10 – 12 mm).	Small, flat, elongated bugs; pale green to yellow or light brown with long, mobile antennae. Very agile insects hiding in the floral buds or in the shade.	Insecticidal test on a tarpaulin as recommended for antestia bugs. Dust or spray with malathion or parathion if more than three to five *Volumnus* species per tree, or more than 15 to 20 *Lygus* species per tree.

Symptoms	Disease	Cause	Control
Withering and blackening of the green tips of the branches and of the leaves nearest to the trunk; the middle part of the bush is mainly affected, with the base and apex remaining healthy.	Die-back.	Physiological disease due to exhaustion of the mineral and carbohydrate reserves of the tree after a heavy yield, or the result of water imbalance in the root/shoot transpiration system following a severe drought.	Control by maintaining good cultivation methods; remove dead wood, undertake restorative pruning, apply balanced organic and mineral manures, protect the soil by mulching or a cover crop, establish windbreaks.
Withering and rapid blackening of the branches, leaves and fruits on all parts of the tree.	Anthracnose; *Colletotrichum coffeanum* (Figs 79 and 80).	Fungal diseases leading to weak growth developing during the rainy season, appearing in a spectacular manner in the dry season. Shoots appear to wither; black fruiting bodies the size of a pinhead appear on the upper side of the leaves and branches. Particularly serious on young trees.	Prevent by proper maintenance and application of balanced manures. Use resistant varieties. Spray with daconil (or other copper based fungicide) where it extends to sensitive varieties.
Blackening and death of the shoots, young leaves and tips of branches, stunted growth. Exaggerated development of secondary branches with short internodes.	Frost damage. Hot and cold disease	Climatic damage at high altitudes, where plants are subject to alternating cold night-time temperatures and hot day-time temperatures.	Where this hazard is greatest, protect the coffee plants with shade trees and windbreaks.
Flower buds with an unusual shape upon opening.	Virescence. Star flowering.	Selections of some species are poorly adapted to the local environment, and this is reflected in premature opening of the flower buds.	Do not grow arabica in low, hot and humid equatorial zones. Use species and varieties which are adapted to the local environment.

Damage – symptoms	Causal agent	Pest or disease characteristics	Control methods
Damage to the foliage			
Generalised defoliation.	Caterpillars of the coffee hawk moth: *Cephonodes hylas* (Fig 69). Giant looper: *Ascotis* spp.	Large day-flying moth up to 65 mm in length, with transparent wings; broad, brownish green thorax and abdomen, ending in a tuft of black hairs; brownish red belt around the abdomen; lays isolated eggs on the underside of the leaves. Green caterpillar with a blue line on the back; orange head, dark brown antennae; active for three weeks before it pupates in the soil.	Manually collect the caterpillars in the event of a very localised attack and before rapid mutiplication. Otherwise, treat with endosulfan (2 l/ha) at the young stages which are the most sensitive. Often present in the nursery where, because of the daily inspection, it is more economical to combat this pest early by hand collection.
Ditto.	Tailed caterpillars: *Epicampoptera* sp. (Fig 68).	Light brown, nocturnal moth with a wing-span of 35 – 40 mm; lays its eggs, which are joined together, in small columns on the leaves; incubation about ten days, then characteristic caterpillars are produced with a thorax swollen by a hump and with a tapering tail; 35 – 40 mm long when fully developed; very active for 30 to 40 days; four to five generations per year.	Regularly survey the edges of the forest and plantation. Treat with endosulfan as soon as the young caterpillars appear, otherwise there will be a rapid multiplication and very serious damage. It is possible to combat the problem biologically by applying a preparation of *Bacillus thuringiensis*, but this requires two to three days before results are obtained; this is often too great a delay where there is a very rapid rate of multiplication.

Symptoms	Pest	Control
Light green, later brown, irregularly shaped, but clearly defined blotches on the lamina of the leaves. The damaged upper epidermis comes away easily when rubbed, revealing numerous, minute, white caterpillars feeding in the parenchyma of the leaf.	Coffee leaf miner. Leucoptera or coffee plant moths. Genus: *Leucoptera*.	Small, silvery moth with a wingspan of 6 mm; fine, narrow wings, fringed with hairs and a dark mark towards the tip. It lays minute, yellow eggs on the leaves; these develop into nymphs in a silky cocoon. This pest is controlled by natural enemies but may multiply rapidly after the effects of insecticidal treatments such as malathion have dissipated. In an infested area, control for three to four months can be achieved by spreading disulfoton granules containing 5 per cent active ingredient at the foot of the bushes at a rate of 5 – 30 g per tree depending on their size. Spray with penetrating insecticides such as parathion at a rate of 600 g of active ingredient per hectare, applying two treatments with an interval of one month between them, or spread malathion granules.
Leaves furrowed with winding subcutaneous galleries with a silvery appearance, wider at one end than at the other.	Undulating moth: *Gracilaria* sp.	Caterpillars of a small moth similar to *Leucoptera* spp. Limited damage since proliferation is rare. Collect and burn the pest-infested leaves.
Leaves partially eaten, sometimes only on the underside.	Stinging caterpillars: Genera: *Parasa*, *Phoma* (Fig 63).	Caterpillar slugs with atrophied feet and bright colours (bright green–blue); produces tubercles bristling with urticaceous hairs; they live hidden on the underside of the leaves. It is easier to collect the cocoons than the caterpillars. Spray or dust with malathion or thiodan if there is rapid multiplication; this is relatively rare.
Flecked, rolled leaves, discoloured in places, crinkly in texture.	Thrips (Fig 74).	Small alate insects, 1.5 – 2 mm long with slender wings fringed with long, very fine cilia. Gregarious, biting and sucking larvae and nymphs on the underside of the leaves. Cut small branches which are attacked. In the event of rapid multiplication, spray with parathion or diazinon. Also present in nurseries and greenhouses.

Damage – symptoms	Causal agent	Pest or disease characteristics	Control methods
Ditto.	Scale insects. Aphids.	See **Damage to shoots and young branches.**	
Extensive defoliation. Veins sometimes left intact.	Stink grasshopper: *Zonocerus variegatus* (Figs 52 and 75).	Brightly coloured polyphagous grasshopper. The adult is green-yellow-red with black legs: female 45 mm, male 55 mm long. Young, wingless larvae are black and yellow. Mature grasshoppers emit a foul-smelling liquid when handled. Larvae live in groups at the top of bushes and disperse to feed on leaves during the day. Abundant in the dry season at the end of which the females lay eggs in the soil (30 – 40 in an egg-case), where they remain to re-appear en masse at the beginning of the next dry season.	Most effectively controlled when young and gregarious by dusting with insecticides such as malathion, early in the morning. On a well-established diversified population, spray with aqueous or oil-based diazinon at rate of 10 – 12 g active ingredient per 100 m^2. Poisoned bait may also be effective e.g. malathion dusted pieces of pawpaw, cassava leaves or maize.
Round, yellow-green patches, oily appearance on the upperside of the leaves with the underside progressively covered with powdery, orange patches which may coalesce, leading to the death of the leaf. Extensive defoliation.	Orange rust: *Hemileia vastatrix* (Figs 34 and 83).	Very serious fungal disease, many types exist; continental distribution. Spores of the fungus germinate in drops of water and the mycelium penetrates into the leaf parenchyma via the stomatic pores on the undersides of the leaves. Internal development period of two to three weeks, followed by fruiting when masses of red spores emerge on the edges of the patches.	Preventive copper treatments: one per month at the beginning and in the middle of the rainy season i.e. five to six per year. 2 – 5 l of spray applied per tree, i.e. Bordeaux mixture, copper oxychloride etc. Preventive, curative, systemic treatments: use oxycarboxin or triadimefon; maximum of two applications per annum to avoid resistance developing. Plant resistant varieties of robusta hybrids such as arabusta, catimor, icatu and hybrids of arabica resistant to several strains of the fungus.

Symptoms	Disease	Description	Control
Weakened trees with leaves having a powdery, pale orange layer on the underside. Damage originating on the lower branches.	Floury rust: *Hemileia coffeicola* (Fig 83).	An insidious and debilitating fungal disease appearing suddenly without any clearly marked preliminary signs; progressive withering of the affected leaves.	Control during cultivation: careful pruning and good manuring. Chemical control: similar to that recommended for orange rust.
Round, brown patches with a grey centre, 3 – 6 mm in diameter, well defined edges, more visible on the uppersides of the leaves.	'Brown eye' disease: *Cercospora coffeicola* (Fig 81).	Cosmopolitan fungal disease, serious in nurseries; the patches increase in size concentrically; they are bordered by brown rings.	See **Damage in the nursery**.
Old leaves with alternate brown-red, grey-green velvety patches on the upper side.	Leprosy: *Cephaleuros virescens*.	Lichenoid association of an alga and a fungus; only affects excessively shaded plants in a humid atmosphere. Also invades branches and trunks on which it can produce cankers.	Prune and burn the areas affected.
Blackening and necrosis of the young leaves and of the fruiting branches.	Anthracnose (Fig 79).		See **Damage in the nursery**.
The undersides of the leaves become covered with a fine, greyish white, smooth and adherent film, which becomes viscous when damp. Subsequently the leaves turn brown and die, become detached from the branch but remain suspended by filaments of the fungus. The fungus can also attack the branches and the fruits.	Linen disease or coffee thread blight: *Corticium koleroga*.	The mycelium of this fungus blocks the stomata of the leaves and inhibits gaseous exchange with the atmosphere. Attack is generally localised in the most humid areas.	Control mainly through cultural methods. Reduce the shade, if present. Prune and burn the affected branches. Improve air circulation by pruning. If the problem persists, treat with calixine (as for pink disease).

Damage – symptoms	Causal agent	Pest or disease characteristics	Control methods
The leaves and branches are covered with white or brown mycelial filaments which adhere closely to the bark or epidermis of the leaves. Drying and browning follow; the dead leaves are retained by the mycelial filaments.	Cobweb disease or white thread: *Marasmius scandens*. Horsehair disease: *Marasmius equicrinus*.	These fungi do not form a continuous film, only heavily branched filaments.	Treatments similar to those used for linen disease.
The leaves are covered in brown circular patches outlined by a clearly darker line. These patches become white, the tissues dry then fall out, leaving the leaf full of holes.	Iron or leaf spot: *Mycena citricolor*.	Very serious, essentially an American fungal disease. Very debilitating due to the way it attacks the laminae of the leaves and the subsequent leaf fall which it produces. Also attacks the fruits.	Control through cultural methods, particularly by improving air circulation in the plantations and the coffee plants by pruning. Artificial defoliation by herbicides may be used in extreme cases to eliminate the inoculum. Preventive copper treatments.
The leaves become discoloured and deformed.	Physiological diseases due to mineral deficiencies.		See section 3.3.

Damage to the fruit

	Damage	Description	Control
Coffee berry borer: *Hypothenemus* (*Stephanoderes*) *hampei* (Figs 58 and 59).	Berries perforated at the opposite end to the stalk, up to 20 larvae may develop from eggs laid in the bean. The tissue of the beans is eaten by larvae. Before the berries develop vitreous or hardened tissue suitable for egg laying, the so-called inter-season females eat the young green berries resulting in their fall. Yield and quality may be severely reduced due to holes made in infested beans.	Very small elongated, oval, dark brown or shiny black cosmopolitan beetle. The males are small and wingless. The female excavates egg-laying holes inside the berries where she lays two to three eggs per day, remaining inside the berry until the eggs have developed into larvae. She then passes to another berry. Larval cycle is approximately 20 days, with a life cycle of less than one month, i.e. seven to eight generations per year. The larvae feed within the dead seeds which fall to the ground and remain in the harvested fruits and beans during storage, provided that their water content is greater than 18 per cent.	Preventive cultivation. Carefully remove infected berries on the tree and on the ground (hygienic harvesting). Dust, spray or sprinkle malathion at a rate of 800 g/ha; two to three applications with intervals of 10 days between them. Alternatively endosulfan at a rate of 1600 g/ha; two applications with an interval of 20 days between them. Apply insecticides to the fruit-bearing branches four months before harvesting to eliminate the inter-season females. There is also a degree of natural control afforded by parasites of the beetle.
Coffee berry moth: *Prophantis smaragdina* (*Thliptocera octoguttalis*). Coffee berry butterfly: *Virachola bimaculata* (Fig 70).	Large perforations made in the cherries which turn yellow and shrivel. Similar damage to the shoots and the young branches.	This small moth with a wingpan of 10 – 15 mm lays its eggs on the flower buds or young berries. The caterpillars make holes in the berries close to the fruit stalk. One caterpillar can damage up to 50 berries. The hole is up to 2 mm in diameter at the exit.	Generally little damage, with the moths often killed by insecticidal treatments against the major predators such as defoliating caterpillars, scolytids, antestia bugs.

Damage – symptoms	Causal agent	Pest or disease characteristics	Control methods
Cherry rot. The fruits drop and the pulp is found to contain small maggots.	Fruit fly: *Ceratitis capitata* (Fig 71).	Small light-coloured fly which lays its eggs on a great number of species of tropical and Mediterranean fruit; development cycle from the egg to the fly is less than one month.	Careful treatment is necessary in view of the rate of spread of the attacks and the fact that the fruits are sprayed at a stage close to their maturity. Parathion is the best short-duration spray and is active against adults and larvae. Attractive, poisoned mixtures such as syrup of sugar or molasses plus malathion may be sprayed onto the branches.
Close to maturity, some fruits disappear; depulped beans are then found on the plantation.	Rodents. *Rattus* sp. or squirrels (Fig 73).	Rodents prefer to attack ripe berries, eating the sweet pulp and leaving the depulped beans which, if they germinate, are called 'rat coffee'.	Poisoned bait such as coumafene: 0.25 g/kg + bran + blood meal or powdered milk.
Bitten, deformed cherries.	Antestia bugs.	See **Damage to the young branches, shoots and flower buds.**	
Berries infested with small whitish, brownish or greenish insects.	Scale insects. Aphids (see page 85).	Ditto.	
The berries have circular, brownish, smooth depressions; they then turn totally black, shrivel and fall or turn to dust when squeezed between the fingers.	Anthracnose of the berries (Coffee Berry Disease: CBD), *Collectrotrichum coffeanum* (Fig 80) (see page 87).	A very virulent, specialised form of the anthracnose fungus, a very serious disease attacking mainly the flower buds and young fruits of arabica grown at high altitudes, at the beginning of the rainy season.	Treatment during cultivation: Apply early irrigation, producing early flowering and fruit development in the dry season, inducing resistance of fruits to attack by the fungus in the rainy season. Spray daconil as a preventive measure. Use resistant varieties.

The berries are covered with a red film, which later becomes white and floury.	Floury or fruit rot: *Trachysphaeria fructigena*. Dangerous fungal disease particularly harmful to the young berries, the development of which is arrested. The mycelium also attacks the branches.	Spray with copper or sulphur/calcium mixtures.
The berries are covered with brown marks with a central split; necrosis develops as they mature. The seed is not affected but the pulp adheres to it, making it difficult to remove.	Cercosporiosis or berry-blotch: *Cercospora coffeicola*. See **Damage to the leaves in the nursery.**	

Damage to the dry berries and stored coffee

The dry berries externally have a regular hole approximately 4 mm in diameter (the exit hole of the adult insect); the interior is filled with a fine powder composed of the excrement of the larva.	False bruchid: *Araeocerus fasciculatus* (Fig 72). Small, oval, convex beetle from 2.5 – 4.5 mm in length; resembles the bean beetle, dark brown to blackish grey in colour, covered with a yellowish to reddish brown pubescence. It is very polyphagous, whitish larva eats into the drying berries, totally emptying them. Several generations are possible in one year; there are sometimes massive infestations.	Preventive treatments: care in the preparation of the beans: avoid crushed berries and dry well. Store in batches separate from other food materials and in premises which are disinfected periodically. Curative measures: fumigate under tarpaulin with methylbromide (1 g/20 l). Dust with malathion (0.5 g per 100 kg).
The beans are eaten away in a manner reminiscent of a Swiss cheese. The edges of the holes are bluish green in colour.	Coffee berry borer: *Hypothenemus (Stephanoderes) hampei* (Figs 30 and 39). See **Damage to the berries.**	Heat the berries before processing. Dry carefully, to leave a water content of less than 13 per cent.

Fig 50   *Coffee berry borer* (Hypothenemus hampei*). Section of a berry with seed containing larvae, nymphs and adults which have just undergone imaginal shedding (BOUL-ARD collection)*

Fig 51   *Larvae, nymph and adult of branch scolytid beetle* (Xyleborus morstatti*) in a small branch of* C. robusta

Fig 52   *A group of young stink grasshoppers* (Zonocerus variegatus*) on* C. robusta. *RCA (BOULARD collection)*

Fig 53   *Fruits attacked by scale insects. RCA (BOULARD collection)*

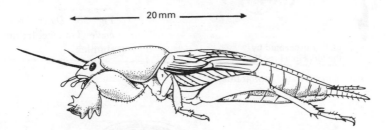

Fig 54   *Mole cricket (*Gryllotalpa africana*)*

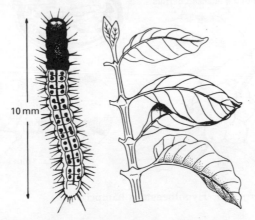

Fig 55   *Leaf-rolling caterpillar (*Lecythocera schoutedeniella*)*

97

Fig 56 *Damage caused by coffee leaf skeletoniser (*Leucoplema dohertyi*)*

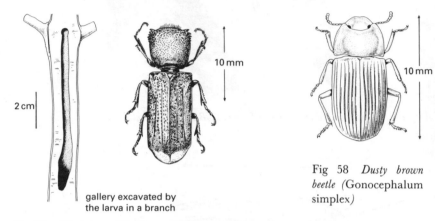

10 mm

2 cm

gallery excavated by
the larva in a branch

Fig 57 *Black borer (*Apate monachus*)*

10 mm

Fig 58 *Dusty brown beetle (*Gonocephalum simplex*)*

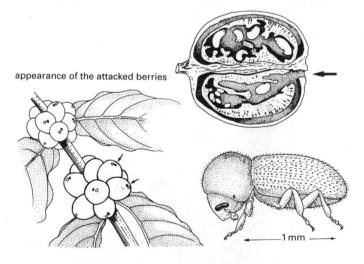

appearance of the attacked berries

1 mm

Fig 59 *Coffee berry borer (*Hypothenemus hampei*)*

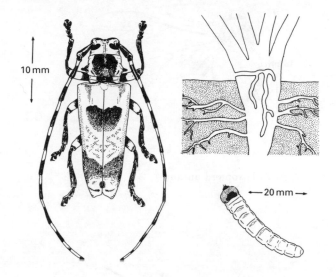

Fig 60   *Trunk borer* (Bixadus sierricola)

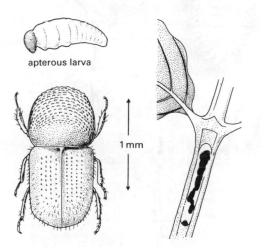

apterous larva

Fig 61   *Branch scolytid beetle* (Xyleborus morstatti)

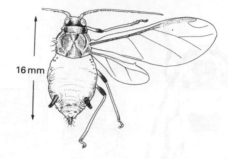

Fig 62   *Coffee plant aphid (*Toxoptera aurantii*)*

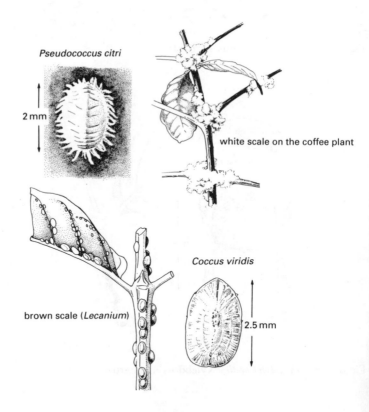

Pseudococcus citri

2 mm

white scale on the coffee plant

brown scale (*Lecanium*)

Coccus viridis

2.5 mm

Fig 63   *Types of scale insect*

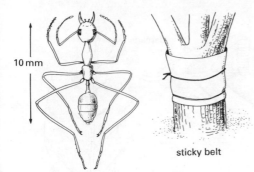

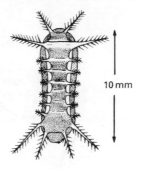

sticky belt

Fig 64   *Red ant (*Oecophylla longinoda*)*

Fig 65   *Stinging cater-pillar (*Phorma pepon*)*

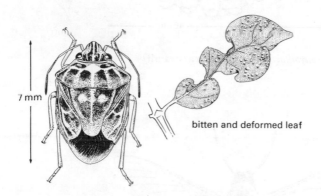

bitten and deformed leaf

Fig 66   *Antestia bug (*Antestiopsis orbitalis*)*

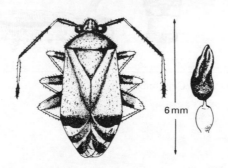

Fig 67   *Mirid (capsid) (*Volumnus obscuris*): appearance of a bitten flower bud*

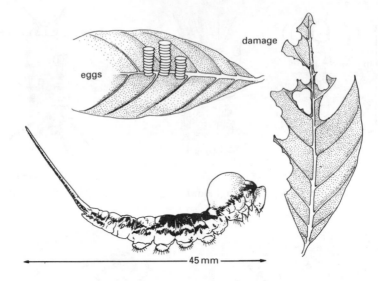

eggs

damage

45 mm

Fig 68   *Tailed caterpillar* (Epicampoptera strandi)

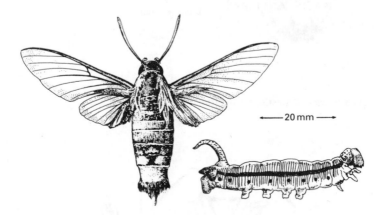

20 mm

Fig 69   *Coffee hawk moth* (Cephonodes hylas)

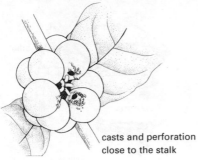

casts and perforation
close to the stalk

Fig 70   *Damage caused by caterpillars of the coffee berry moth (*Prophantis smaragdina*)*

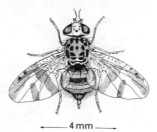

4 mm

Fig 71   *Fruit fly (*Ceratitis capitata*)*

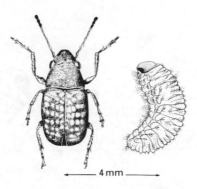

4 mm

Fig 72   *False bruchid and its larva (*Araeocerus fasciculatus*)*

Fig 73   *Rat (*Rattus *sp.) eating the ripe cherries*

103

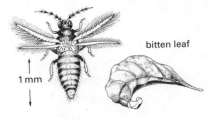

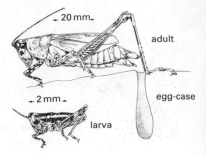

Fig 74 *Thrips (*Heliothrips rubrocinctus*)*

Fig 75 *Stink grasshopper (*Zonocerus variegatus*)*

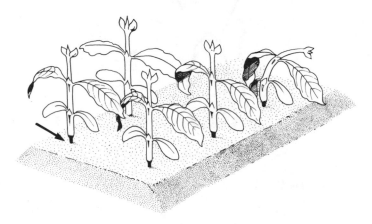

Fig 76 *Damping-off in the nursery (strangulation of the stem at the collar)*

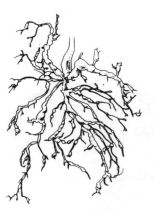

Fig 77 *Root nodules: a result of infestation by nematodes*

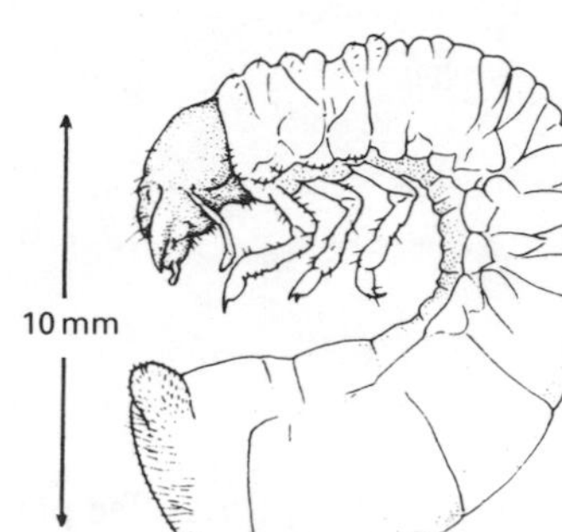

10 mm

Fig 78   *White grub: cock-chafer larva*

Fig 79   *Anthracnose (*Colletotrichum coffeanum*): appearance of the damage caused to the leaves*

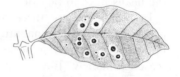

Fig 81   *'Brown eye' disease* (Cercospora coffeicola*)*

Fig 80   *Appearance of cherries caused by anthracnose: coffee berry disease* (Colletotrichum coffeanum*)*

Hemileia coffeicola
Hemileia vastatrix

H. vastatrix
1st stage

leaf about to fall

Fig 82   *Thread blight (*Corticium koleroga*)*

Fig 83   *Coffee plant rusts*

105

6 Harvesting

This takes place at the end of the annual growth cycle of the coffee plant and varies according to the species grown (arabica: 6 – 8 months, robusta: 10 – 11 months) and its location in terms of latitude and altitude.

For robusta, the harvesting period generally corresponds with the end of the rainy season and the beginning of the dry season, i.e. from November to January in the northern equatorial zone. Coffee processing is more difficult when harvesting is carried out in the middle of the rainy season, as in the case of arabica grown in high-altitude equatorial areas, since the beans have to be dried.

In regions where there are four seasons, there are two harvesting periods of unequal magnitude, corresponding to the ends of cycles initiated by flowering periods at the ends of the short and long dry seasons, namely July to August and December to February in the northern hemisphere.

A time difference of six months occurs in the southern hemisphere, making the harvesting periods of the two hemispheres complementary. A country such as Colombia, where the coffee-growing regions are divided by the equator and are at greatly differing altitudes, has its coffee production spread over the entire year.

For arabica, the following flowering and harvesting times apply:

Regions of cultivation

Northern latitude	Flowering	Harvesting
El Salvador (14N–87°W)	April to May	November to February
Ethiopia (8N–36°E)	February to April	October to December
Kenya (1N/1S–36°E)	September to December	May to July
	February to May	September to December

Southern latitude	Flowering	Harvesting
Zimbabwe (18S–30°E)	August to October	End of May to beginning of September
New Caledonia (21S–163°E)	September to November	May to July
Brazil (São Paulo) (22S–48°W)	September to October	April to August

Harvesting is a very labour-intensive operation, whether on a small or commercial scale. It is staggered to various degrees, according to the variety and the climate at the time of flowering, although floral initiation and multiple flowering is possible when there has been a succession of short dry periods followed by adequate rain. This staggering is sometimes harmful from the economic point of view, in that it continuously mobilises the labour necessary to ensure high-quality harvesting for approximately three months (one picking round on each plot every ten to fifteen days). It is, on the other hand, advantageous when it involves the full-time use of a permanent labour-force reserve.

The fundamental principle which should guide the conscientious grower is that the fruits should be picked only when they have reached optimum maturity i.e. the colour should be a good red, not yellow or dark brown. This means that selective picking has to be carried out manually fruit by fruit, as it cannot yet be done by the various mechanical harvesting systems currently available such as motor-driven, back-carried, agitator-beating machines, automatic feeling machines, self-driven vibrating machines and straddling machines of the type used for harvesting grapes. These are generally limited in their use by the maximum height of the bushes to be straddled (2.5 m), the pruning system used and the slope of the ground.

Regrettably, a poor harvesting practice has been on the increase for some years now, involving the early harvesting of the fruits before they are fully mature. Among the reasons given for this are the fear of theft of ripe cherries from the plant and demands for accelerated repayment of advances made to the producers by the agents of commercial firms. Whatever the case, at this stage of prematurity where the cherry is still green, the seeds are insufficiently developed and under-weight and the chemical elements which generate the typical coffee aroma are not yet present. The effect of such a practice on the quality of the beverage is very significant and steps should be taken to stop it.

> *Harvesting green, immature fruit harms the planter since the seeds are not completely developed; this adversely affects the quality of the beverage.*

Manual picking with the aid of
a bag at waist level

Improved manual picking using
a collecting mat

Fig 84   *Manual harvesting*

The manual harvesting methods recommended are:
- Picking into a harvesting bag at waist level (Fig 84);
- Picking using a harvesting mat (jute or thick plastic) arranged under the bushes. This frees both hands for selective but rapid picking of the red fruits and gives a 30 per cent improvement in the harvesting yield compared with the traditional method (Fig 84).

In both these methods, the cherries are collected in a plastic bucket and carried to the end of the row where they are emptied into a harvesting sack.

It is generally easier to pick arabica than canephora since, when they have reached maturity, even a gust of wind can induce them to drop. This demonstrates the need for frequent picking rounds so as to avoid having to collect soiled fruits from the ground.

An essential precaution: the cherries should not be stored for long periods in piles or in bulk because there is a risk of overheating which can lead to the beans being bruised, accompanied by a whole series of fermentations, ranging from the production of fruity aromas to fetid odours and the formation of black seeds.

Yield

The yield of the plots will vary according to the species or variety grown, the layout of the plantation, the climate and the prevailing growing conditions of the year (in particular those of the pruning cycle). The age of the bushes is also significant, since yield increases from three years to eight years, then becomes stable and finally falls off after fifteen years.

Robusta yield is generally considered to be:
- **Poor**: when it is below 300 kg of clean coffee per hectare (i.e. less than 1500 kg of fresh fruits per hectare);
- **Average**: when it is between 400 and 800 kg of clean coffee per hectare (i.e. 2000 to 4000 kg of fresh fruits per hectare);
- **Good**: when it is between 900 and 1400 kg of clean coffee per hectare (i.e. 4500 to 7000 kg of fresh fruits per hectare);
- **Very good**: when it is between 1500 and 2000 kg of clean coffee per hectare (i.e. 7500 to 10 000 kg of fresh fruits per hectare);
- **Excellent**: when it is above 2000 kg of clean coffee per hectare (i.e. more than 100 000 kg of fresh fruits per hectare).

Average yields for arabica are:
- **Poor**: when it is below 500 kg of clean coffee per hectare;
- **Average**: when it is between 500 and 1000 kg of clean coffee per hectare;
- **Good**: when it is between 1000 and 1500 kg of clean coffee per hectare;
- **Very good**: when it is between 1500 and 2000 kg of clean coffee per hectare;
- **Excellent**: when it is above 2000 kg of clean coffee per hectare.

The daily picking rate of harvesters varies in an almost linear manner with the yield of the plots, i.e. between 0.2 and 1 tonne per hectare.

The cost of picking is the main element in the total production costs of marketable coffee, often exceeding 50 per cent of this total. It is therefore essential that serious attention is paid to organising the picking so that these costs are kept as low as possible.

Phytosanitary harvestings, which are carried out before or after the main harvest, aim to remove any over-ripe cherries which are likely to serve either as food for pests such as scolytid beetles, or as a substrate for fungi which are harmful to the trees. They are also a sensible precaution for safeguarding the future of the plots. Given that their relative cost is quite high, as they involve a relatively small number of cherries, it is understandable, regrettably, that they are not carried out as often as they should be.

Glossary

Acclimatisation   To induce a plant to become accustomed, in stages, to a new climatic environment.

Acuminate   Leaf tapering gradually to a point.

Affinity   Applies to a species or variety having morphological and/or biological characteristics which resemble another species or variety.

Alate   Winged, adult insect; wingless forms also occuring.

Anatropous   Ovule curved in the ovarian loculus or carpel.

Anthracnose   Dark, sunken, necrotic disease lesion.

Auger   A metal instrument with a spiral head or a gimlet for boring holes in wood or earth. The pedologist's auger, which is small in diameter, enables him to extract core samples of sub-soil revealing the different layers. The larger diameter auger, driven mechanically by a petrol or diesel engine operated by two men or carried on a power take-off from a tractor, enables holes to be made for planting bushes.

Autogamous   Self-pollinating.

Axil   The angle between a leaf and the stem from which it arises.

Back-crossing   Crossing a hybrid with one of its parents or with plant of the same genetic constitution as the parent.

Bud-bearing branch   Stem or part of a stem left after cutting back (stump pruning) to reduce the physiological shock to the plant by this severe pruning.

Calcomagnesium   Fertiliser containing both lime and magnesium.

Canopy   Branch framework and foliage of a tree or bush.

Capping   Cutting the top off an orthotropic stem.

CBD   Coffee Berry Disease; a fungal disease attacking the cherries of the coffee plant, caused by a virulent form of *Colletrotrichum coffeanum*.

Chlorosis   Yellowing of the foliage.

Clay-humus complex   All the clay-type materials and components of humus which regulate the functions of absorption and release of the chemical constituents of the soil.

Clean-weeding   A horticultural term meaning the total removal of all weeds by hoeing or manual uprooting.

110

Coleoptera   Order of insects called beetles, having biting mouthparts and hard or leathery forewings.

Collar   Region where roots change to stem at soil level.

Colloidal complex   All of the fine materials which are in suspension in the soil solution.

Cordate   Heart-shaped.

Coriaceous   Leathery.

Cross-fertilisation   State of sexual reproduction of a plant or group of plants which can only be fertilised by pollen from a different individual.

Cultivar   Selected variety (cultivated variety) normally a hybrid, widely used commercially.

Cutting-back   Pruning the stems and branches to reduce their height or length.

Cytogenetic   Detailed study of the genes responsible for the transmission of hereditary characteristics.

Die-back   Horticultural term commonly used to describe progressive withering of the branches of a bush, starting with the extremities and advancing towards the trunk, due to the effect of a physiological or pathogenic disorder.

Dwarfing (as in rootstocks)   Species or varieties used for their restricted growth potential as in high density planting.

Ecological complex   All of the natural elements making up the environment such as fauna, flora and physical environment including soil and climate.

Endosperm   Mass of nutritive tissue surrounding the embryo within the seed.

Enzymology   Physico-chemical study enabling an individual, a variety or a species to be characterised by the identity and diversity of its enzymatic constituents.

Eradication   Complete removal.

Evapotranspiration   Water lost from the surface of plants by evaporation through the stomata.

Exserting   Stamens protruding from the tube of the corolla as a result of filament extension.

Floral induction   Initiation of the development of the flower buds.

Hardening off   An acclimatisation phase during which seedlings or cuttings colonise a new rooting medium and adjust to an environment, e.g. the drier atmosphere of a shaded area.

Harvesting or picking bag   A paper or plastic bag tied to the waist, the bottom opening of which is secured by wire or a rigid piece of creeper.

Heterosis (hybrid vigour)   An increase in vigour, growth or yield of a hybrid progeny in relation to the average performance of either of the parents.

Inferior   As in the flower when the ovary is sited below the level of insertion of the floral parts (calyx and corolla).

In-vitro plant Plantlet produced by an artifical process of multiplication in glass (in-vitro) or in plastic test tubes and immersed in a nutrient solution.

Land clearance Clearance of the plots of felled and chain-sawn logs of wood by placing them in swaths in the inter-rows or edges of the plantation.

Metabolism Changes in the chemical and physico-chemical constituents of the tissues which comprise a living plant or other organism.

Moisture status The water content within the plant, normally obtained from the soil solution and lost by transpiration through the stomata in the epidermal layer of the leaves.

Multiple-stemmed Having several stems.

Necrosis Death and resulting breakdown of the tissues.

Nematode Non-segmented round worm; plant parasitic forms are microscopic.

Orthotropic Stem which grows vertically upwards.

Percolation Loss of excess water and chemical elements in solution through the sub-soil layer where they are absorbed by the roots of plants.

Pericarp The fruit wall which develops from the ovary wall.

Perisperm Layers of nutritive tissue derived from the nucellus and the embryo.

pH Number indicating the level of soil acidity or alkalinity; below seven indicates an acid soil, above seven indicates alkaline or basic, with a neutral soil having a pH of approximately seven.

Phenology Study of the various events in the development of the plant.

Photosynthesis Production of carbohydrates as a result of the action of light energy.

Phytosanitary harvesting Early or late harvesting to remove fruits which mature out of season, with the objective of reducing the incidence of pests or disease.

Plagiotropic Tending to grow horizontally or obliquely, as in the branches of coffee.

Polyphagous Having many different food plants.

Post-emergence After appearing at the surface, during the early growth period of seedlings, usually used in reference to chemical weed control.

Pre-emergence The stage before seedling emergence at the soil surface.

Regeneration 1 Resumption of cultivation of a plot beginning with replacement of all the missing trees to restore the original density.

Regeneration 2 New development of buds or shoots after the growth of a first series.

Relative humidity The actual quantity of water contained in a given volume of air expressed as a percentage of the maximum amount that could be present at the same temperature.

Rotary crushing   Weeding or stubble-ploughing using an agricultural machine fitted with flails or blades rotating horizontally under a housing.

Self-sterility   Situation where it is impossible for the flowers of a plant or group of plants to be fertilised by their own pollen.

Sessile   Without a stalk.

Shedding   Fruits fall before maturity.

Spacer   Stick cut into a V-shape at its two ends, intended to keep multiple stems apart.

Straddling machine   Agricultural machine with a suspension system which allows it to pass along two inter-rows over the row or rows of fruiting coffee.

Substrate   Artificial mixture of free-draining material serving as a medium for rooting cuttings.

Swathing   Piling up plant debris in rows during land clearance.

Synchronous   Occurring simultaneously: applied to the flowering of trees of different varieties or clones blooming during the same period.

Trace element   Mineral chemical component necessary for plant health but present in very small quantities.

Vapour pressure   Pressure at which, for a given temperature, the liquid phase is in equilibrium with the gaseous phase.

Bibliography

References and further reading

Clowes, M. (1981) *Coffee handbook* (Coffee Growers Association, Salisbury, Zimbabwe)

Mwangi, C. N. (1983) *Coffee growers handbook* (Coffee Research Foundation, Ruiru, Kenya)

Anonymous (1976) *Coffee pests and their control* (Coffee Research Foundation, Ruiru, Kenya)

Index

Page numbers in *italics* refer to illustrations or tables.